The Fifth **GREENBOOK®** Guide To **Department 56** Villages

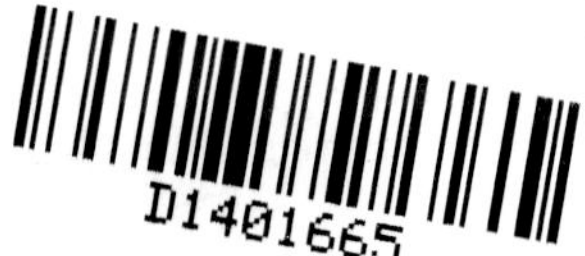

THE ORIGINAL SNOW VILLAGE©

THE HERITAGE VILLAGE COLLECTION™

Dickens' Village
New England Village
Alpine Village
Christmas In The City
Little Town Of Bethlehem
North Pole
Disney Park Village

& ACCESSORIES

The Most Respected Guides to Popular Collectibles & Their After Market Values

Old Coach at Main, Box 515
East Setauket, New York 11733
516.689.8466
FAX 516.689.8177

ISBN 0-923628-25-8

GREENBOOK TRUMARKET PRICES are obtained from retailers and collectors. Manufacturers verify factual information only and are not consulted or involved in any way in determining GREENBOOK TRUMARKET Prices.

ACKNOWLEDGEMENTS

The GREENBOOK would like to thank -

Department 56 for assisting in the compilation of the factual information contained in this Guide.

The collectors, dealers, exchanges, newsletters and magazines across the country who supply us with information including secondary market status and prices.

NOTE FROM THE PUBLISHER

This is GREENBOOK'S Tenth Anniversary. For five of those years we've published the GREENBOOK Guide To DEPARTMENT 56 Collectibles. Doing the D56 Guide changed life at GREENBOOK, so, even though it was difficult, we look back at the First Edition with much affection.

It was the only Department 56 Guide to feature a photographed, rather than illustrated, cover.

Dissatisfied with the coarseness of the "real plastic snow," our photographer replaced it with salt. It's July. We're 'doing' the book during one of the East Coast's prolonged hot and humid heat waves. In a few short days there was water dripping from under the table, and the crusted salt around the base of each building really did resemble Mid-West snow after an ice storm. Cleaning up the mess, we joked of the margaritas the salt would have enhanced!

If you own previous editions of the Guide you know that Tree is a four-letter word at GREENBOOK. This also stems (sorry) from our First Edition experiences. The Guide was literally on the press when we received yet another call with additional corrections. Our solution: The now semi-famous "We saw the forest, we missed a few trees" bookmark. It's funny now. It wasn't then.

Our first illustrated cover, for our Second Edition, showcased *Christmas In The City*. The inspiration came from a Christmas card. I loved the artist's work and asked if she could execute a Village portrait. The result was beyond my expectations. For me, the illustrations bring the Villages to life. Still, I was nervous and thought it a huge risk not to use an actual piece on the cover. My fears were quickly laid to rest at a special show for Retailers. A blowup of the cover was displayed in our booth and everyone asked for lithographs. There was even a request to use the art as a billboard!

The subject of this year's Fifth Edition cover couldn't be more appropriate if we'd planned in advance. The Original Snow Village is enjoying a booming resurgence in the marketplace. The reason given by collectors is so simple it's almost boring ... "the new pieces are fabulous!"

I've always said the one thing that makes Department 56 Villages different from other contemporary collectibles is that often the entire family is involved. I've lost count of the number of people who tell me they collect one or two villages and their kids collect, you guessed it, North Pole Village.

Over the past year I've realized there's something else. One building begets another. Almost anyone can visualize one or two of those cute little lighted houses on the mantel or under the tree as a holiday decoration. Ah, but of course, if you're reading this, you know how innocently it starts.

As a matter of fact, there's a person in our office experiencing the "morphing into a collector" phenomenon right now. This is the same person who, not too long ago, delicately suggested some of us should consider "getting a life." Now we have a video of her, taken during the recent National Association Of Limited Edition Dealers Awards Banquet, explaining even though she'd just purchased a *Santa's Workshop* for more than $300, she's not a collector. Right! We'll keep you posted.

The enclosed Original Snow Village and Heritage Village Collection GREENBOOK WISHLISTS are our Tenth Anniversary Gift to you. In the planning stage they were to be a simple, portable, personal inventory and "cheat sheet" of the Guide. They evolved into much more. By dividing each Village into what's available at retail and what's not, we'd hoped to save non-collecting family and friends hours of frustration as they shop for the perfect gift for you.

The added benefit is At-A-Glance insight into exactly how many pieces are available at SRP (Suggested Retail Price), what current pieces have been available the longest, what percentage have been retired and what a gift giver should expect to pay. Additional copies of the WISHLIST can be purchased from your retailer.

More excitement! A new GREENBOOK GUIDE TO DEPARTMENT 56 COLLECTIBLES debuts this year. Developed in response to growing demand, the book showcases Snowbabies. Also featured are Snowbunnies, Winter Silhouette, All Through The House, Merry Makers, Upstairs Downstairs Bears, Mercury Glass Ornaments, CCP's, Waterglobes, **Music Boxes,** Village Related Ornaments and other additional varied items like dolls, plates, buttons and paper products. It too is available from your favorite retailer.

Just a reminder: If you'd like a Bookmark Update of Retirements, send us an empty, self-addressed, stamped, business size envelope marked D56 UPDATE in the lower left corner. We print right after the announcement. Books reprinted after retirement have the bookmark inside the shrinkwrap.

I'm almost finished.

Before closing, I'd like to thank the members of NALED (National Association Of Limited Edition Dealers) for presenting us with an Award Of Excellence for our contributions to collecting. It's an honor to have one's work recognized and applauded. We truly appreciate the NALED Award, and we also thank you, the collector, for your support over the past decade. We hope you continue to find the GREENBOOK a great asset to collecting. Please let us know if you have any suggestions, comments or complaints. We're committed to being the best and that will only happen with your input. Thank you for purchasing the Guide,

Louise Patterson Langenfeld
Editor and Publisher

TABLE OF CONTENTS

HOW TO USE THIS GUIDE

The GREENBOOK ARTCHART & LISTINGS contain exclusive GREENBOOK line drawings as well as specific factual information and GREENBOOK TRUMARKET Prices for each piece.

Factual information includes Title, Description, Year Of Introduction, Item Number, Material, Is it part of a Set and if so the number of pieces comprising the set, Is it Lighted?, Market Status or specific edition limit, and the Original Suggested Retail Price.

Secondary Market Prices, as reported by retailers and collectors, are included as well. Because there are so many factors based on individual judgements, and because prices can vary depending on time of year or section of the country, **GREENBOOK TRUMARKET Prices are never an absolute number**. Use them as a benchmark.

The Guide is divided into three main sections: The Original Snow Village and its accessories, The Heritage Village Collection and Heritage Village Accessories and Additional Village Accessories, aka Trees & Trim. Within the Snow Village and Heritage Village sections, GREENBOOK Listings are in chronological date of introduction order. It's important to remember "the year of introduction indicates the year in which the piece was designed, sculpted, and copyrighted" and the piece is generally available to collectors the following calendar year.

Within each year the listings are in Department 56 Item Number order.

Each piece has been assigned a GREENBOOK ARTCHART Number comprised of a coded alphabetic prefix (SV = Snow Village, CIC = Christmas In The City, etc.), followed by year of introduction, and then a sequential number.

If you know the name of the piece but not the year of introduction, use the Name/D56 Item #/Page # Index in the back of the Guide to locate the piece.

Variations and comments are noted in the shaded area of each listing. And in most cases there's room for your own notes as well.

Peter George

GREENBOOK extends a hearty welcome to noted Department 56 authority, Peter George. Peter and his wife Jeanne publish the Village Chronicle, a bimonthly magazine. (That's every two months for those, like me, who are never sure exactly what that means.) The magazine is chock-full of interesting tidbits of information that make collecting more fun. This is the second year that Peter shares his wit and wisdom with GREENBOOK readers, as our Department 56 Historian.

Hello again! The past year just flew by. But then, with the amount of traveling that Jeanne and I do throughout the year, it's no wonder that time goes by so fast. By far, the best thing about traveling is that we have the opportunity to meet so many wonderful collectors. This is one of the reasons that we do so much of our traveling by car. In route to and from Gatherings, open houses, club events and the like, we enjoy stopping to visit friends we've made through this great hobby. Needless to say, we have just as much fun stopping at collectible stores and gift and Christmas shops. Searching for retired houses is a never ending process ... and a fun one. You can't do that when you're 30,000 feet in the air.

Your response to last year's GREENBOOK Historian segments was very positive. Your comments and ideas, and certainly your well wishes, made working on this Fifth Edition exciting.

So, what have I been up to for the past year besides attending events? Most of my time was spent publishing and writing for our magazine, *the Village Chronicle*. My remaining time was divided between working with GREENBOOK and squeezing some time in for collecting. Like you, Jeanne and I continue to pursue our love for these wonderful buildings and accessories created by D56. Keeping our collection going seems like a full-time job. We collect Dickens' Village, North Pole and Christmas In The City. I guess it's easier to say I collect Dickens' and Jeanne collects the rest of D56 including pieces from each village (Alpine was a recent addition). But it doesn't stop there. Our collection also includes Snowbabies, Snowbunnies, Merry Makers, Lite-Ups, CCP's, Winter Silhouette, waterglobes and music boxes, Upstairs Downstairs Bears, D56 Ted D. Bears and snowmen, and a variety of D56 giftware and ornaments. To answer an often asked question, no, we do not have every piece of every collection ... just those we like.

Enjoy the book and I hope to see you at an event soon. If you have the opportunity, come say hello. I really enjoy talking with collectors, trading stories and seeing pictures of displays. Until then ...

May your home be merry and your houses be many,

Peter

Quite often we hear collectors who are attending a major event for the first time say that they are surprised, if not dismayed, by the long lines that they encounter. If long lines have made you think twice about attending an event, look at it this way, at least they aren't like lines at the bank. At a bank most people just want to get in and out and generally do not speak to others in line. But at a collectible event, and more specifically, a D56 event, we all have something in common. Take the lines in stride. The only reason the lines are so long is because you enjoy something that thousands of others love as well. So, relax and strike up a conversation with your temporary neighbor. The easiest way to do it is ask, "What do you collect?" You'll be through the line in no time.

I was asked to be the guest speaker at a recent Collectors Club Anniversary Party. During dinner, Jeanne and I had occasion to be seated at a table with a very nice group. After the introductions were made, we told each other a little about ourselves and what we collected. One woman informed us that she was a collector, but her significant other was not. When another collector asked him why he had come he replied he was there for the shrimp cocktail and prime rib dinner. Though the dinner was very good and he enjoyed it, those items were not on the menu. And the lady? She just smiled.

Grab it when you see it; it's as simple as that. I often give this advice, but taking it myself is a different story. Last year at a large Swap & Sell, I saw two pieces of the Dickens' Village Original 7 Shops sitting on a table. Each was priced at $60.00. I checked the price tags again to be sure that I had read them correctly. Then I looked up to get Jeanne's attention. In that split second, another shopper put their hands on them and said, "I'll take these." The lesson from this story: If you see something that interests you, pick it up and then decide if you really want to buy it. That way you won't be kicking yourself as you walk on down the aisle.

continued on page 106

1976 THE ORIGINAL SNOW VILLAGE 1976

SV76-1

MOUNTAIN LODGE

Bright colored skis lean against two-story lodge, upper windows painted to appear as lead panes, sunburst painted above door, snow laden tree at side.

SV76-2

GABLED COTTAGE

Four-peaked roof with two chimneys, curtained windows, welcome mat. Ivy climbs walls to roof and door & several windows have wreath design. Snow laden tree with bluebird.

SV76-3

THE INN

Two large brick chimneys, full length covered porch, welcome mat at timbered front doors, snow laden tree on one side, bright yellow door on opposite side.

SV76-4

COUNTRY CHURCH

Vines and painted welcome on walls, short-spired, door ajar, circular upper windows, painted side windows, snow laden tree shades one wall.

SV76-5

STEEPLED CHURCH

One spire, large circular window over double wood front doors flanked by leaded lattice design windows, side Chapel, snow covered tree, bluebird on steeple.

SV76-6

SMALL CHALET

Two-story small gingerbread look home, flower box with snow covered plants set off large windows on upper story. Bluebirds decorate corners of flower box, chimney, tree.

ART CHART #	NAME	ITEM #	MATERIAL	SET?	💡	MARKET STATUS	ORIGINAL SRP	GREENBOOK TRUMKT PRICE
	VARIATIONS/MISC/COLLECTOR NOTES							
SV76-1	MOUNTAIN LODGE	5001-3	Ceramic	NO	✓	RETIRED 1979	$ 20.00	$ 375.00
SV76-2	GABLED COTTAGE	5002-1	Ceramic	NO	✓	RETIRED 1979	20.00	350.00
SV76-3	THE INN	5003-9	Ceramic	NO	✓	RETIRED 1979	20.00	450.00
SV76-4	COUNTRY CHURCH	5004-7	Ceramic	NO	✓	RETIRED 1979	18.00	385.00
	Also known as "Wayside Chapel."							
SV76-5	STEEPLED CHURCH	5005-4	Ceramic	NO	✓	RETIRED 1979	25.00	625.00
SV76-6	SMALL CHALET	5006-2	Ceramic	NO	✓	RETIRED 1979	15.00	400.00
	Also known as "Gingerbread Chalet." Variation in number of flowers in box and color - tan to dark brown.							

CLIPBOARD

- "Original 6" pieces characterized by simple design, rough construction, and bright colors.
- All have attached snow laden evergreen trees with unique feature – bulb that lights house also lights tree.
- The "Gabled Cottage" and "The Inn" were the first Original Snow Village pieces to put out the welcome mats.

1977 THE ORIGINAL SNOW VILLAGE 1977

SV77-1

VICTORIAN HOUSE

Textured to portray shingles and clapboard. Steps lead up to front door. Stained glass inserts above windows. Attached snow laden evergreen tree.

SV77-2

MANSION

White brick with porch supported by pillars, windows are shuttered, two chimneys plus cupola on roof. Attached snow laden evergreen tree.

SV77-3

STONE CHURCH

Norman style stone building, steeple with ceramic bell. Double doors with circular window above, snow laden evergreen tree.

ART CHART #	NAME	ITEM #	MATERIAL	SET?	!	MARKET STATUS	ORIGINAL SRP	GREENBOOK TRUMKT PRICE
	VARIATIONS/MISC/COLLECTOR NOTES							
SV77-1	VICTORIAN HOUSE	5007-0	Ceramic	NO	✓	RETIRED 1979	$ 30.00	$ 455.00
	Variations in color, with and without three birds on roof, and with and without attached tree.							
SV77-2	MANSION	5008-8	Ceramic	NO	✓	RETIRED 1979	30.00	495.00
	Variations in roof color.							
SV77-3	STONE CHURCH	5009-6	Ceramic	NO	✓	RETIRED 1979	35.00	625.00
	This is the original Stone Church. Size is 10.5". Ceramic bell is separate, attached by wire. See 1979, #5059-1 (SV79-6) and 1982, #5083-0 (SV82-10).							

CLIPBOARD

- Broader range of architectural styles, moved away from simple country village style.
- New building materials.
- Again, all had attached snow laden evergreen trees.

1978 THE ORIGINAL SNOW VILLAGE 1978

SV78-1

HOMESTEAD

Old fashioned farmhouse, front porch full length of house. Second floor bay windows. Triple window in front gable. Attached tree.

SV78-2

GENERAL STORE

Full length porch supported by pillars. Sign above porch. Christmas tree on porch roof. Store supplied food, postal service & gas.

SV78-3

CAPE COD

Steep gabled roof with chimney, small dormer, and painted landscaping. Attached snow laden tree.

SV78-4

NANTUCKET

Yellow cottage with green roof. Small front porch, attached greenhouse/sunroom on side, attached snow laden tree.

SV78-5

SKATING RINK/ DUCK POND SET

One large snow laden tree with snowman and log pile. Other large snow laden tree with park bench and birds.

SV78-6

SMALL DOUBLE TREES

Small lighted snow laden trees with birds.

ART CHART #	NAME	ITEM #	MATERIAL	SET?	!	MARKET STATUS	ORIGINAL SRP	GREENBOOK TRUMKT PRICE
	VARIATIONS/MISC/COLLECTOR NOTES							
SV78-1	HOMESTEAD	5011-2	Ceramic	NO	✓	RETIRED 1984	$ 30.00	$ 250.00
SV78-2	GENERAL STORE	5012-0	Ceramic	NO	✓	RETIRED 1980	25.00	See Below
	Variations in color affect price: white @ $450, tan @ $585, and gold @ $550. Also variation in sign lettering: "Y & L" and "S & L Brothers."							
SV78-3	CAPE COD	5013-8	Ceramic	NO	✓	RETIRED 1980	20.00	375.00
SV78-4	NANTUCKET	5014-6	Ceramic	NO	✓	RETIRED 1986	25.00	275.00
	See "Nantucket Renovation," 1993, #5441-0 (SV93-1).							
SV78-5	SKATING RINK/ DUCK POND SET	5015-3	Ceramic	SET OF 2	✓	RETIRED 1979	16.00	1000.00
	One of first non-house accessory pcs. (Skating Rink is piece with snowman.) Trees were attached directly to pond bases - their size and weight caused frequent breakage, therefore retired in 1979. Revised skating pond in 1982, #5017-2 (SV82-1), with trees molded separately.							
SV78-6	SMALL DOUBLE TREES	5016-1	Ceramic	NO	✓	RETIRED 1989	13.50	50.00
	One of the first non-house accessory pieces. First w/blue birds, then red birds. GREENBOOK TRUMARKET PRICE for blue birds is $175. Mold changes and variations in amount of snow over the years as well. Approximately 8 to 8-1/2" tall.							

CLIPBOARD

• New designs reflected a regional influence (New England).

SV79-1

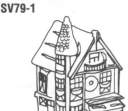

VICTORIAN

Steps lead to covered porch entry, three story turret, small balcony on third floor front room.

SV79-2

KNOB HILL

Three story San Francisco-style Victorian row house, steep steps to entry level.

SV79-3

BROWNSTONE

Three stories with wreath trimmed bay windows on all floors, overall flat roof.

SV79-4

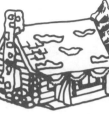

LOG CABIN

Rustic log house with stone chimney, roof extends to cover porch, log pile at side, skis by door.

SV79-5

COUNTRYSIDE CHURCH

White clapboard church with central bell steeple, attached tree has all lower branches pruned.

SV79-6

STONE CHURCH

Steeple attached to one side has separate entry. Circular window above front doors.

SV79-7

SCHOOL HOUSE

American flag flies from roof peak above red brick one-room school.

SV79-8

TUDOR HOUSE

Brick chimney and fireplace on simple L-shaped timber trimmed home, split-shingle roof.

ART CHART #	NAME	ITEM #	MATERIAL	SET?	!	MARKET STATUS	ORIGINAL SRP	GREENBOOK TRUMKT PRICE
	VARIATIONS/MISC/COLLECTOR NOTES							
SV79-1	VICTORIAN	5054-2	Ceramic	NO	✓	RETIRED 1982	$ 30.00	$ 350.00
	Variations in color and exterior finish. They are - in order of desirability - peach, gold, and gold clapboard.							
SV79-2	KNOB HILL	5055-9	Ceramic	NO	✓	RETIRED 1981	30.00	See Below
	Two color variations: gray @ $295 and yellow @ $375.							
SV79-3	BROWNSTONE	5056-7	Ceramic	NO	✓	RETIRED 1981	36.00	575.00
	Variations in roof color: gray and red. Red most desired.							
SV79-4	LOG CABIN	5057-5	Ceramic	NO	✓	RETIRED 1981	22.00	475.00
SV79-5	COUNTRYSIDE CHURCH	5058-3	Ceramic	NO	✓	RETIRED 1984	27.50	295.00
	For no snow version see MEADOWLAND 1979, #5051-8, (MDW79-2).							
SV79-6	STONE CHURCH	5059-1	Ceramic	NO	✓	RETIRED 1980	32.00	1000.00
	Height is 8.5". Ceramic bell is separate, attaches with wire. See 1977, #5009-6 (SV77-3) and 1982, #5083-0 (SV82-10).							
SV79-7	SCHOOL HOUSE	5060-9	Ceramic*	NO	✓	RETIRED 1982	30.00	345.00
	First design to feature the American flag. *Removable metal flag.							
SV79-8	TUDOR HOUSE	5061-7	Ceramic	NO	✓	RETIRED 1981	25.00	325.00

SV79-9

MISSION CHURCH
Sun dried clay with structural timbers visible at roof line. Small arched bell tower above entry.

SV79-10

MOBILE HOME
Similar to aluminum skinned Airstream mobile home. To be towed by car or truck for travel.

SV79-11

GIANT TREES
Snow covered large evergreen trees. Birds perch on branches.

SV79-12

ADOBE HOUSE
Small sundried clay home. Outside oven on side, chili peppers hang from roof beams.

ART CHART #	NAME	ITEM #	MATERIAL	SET?	!	MARKET STATUS	ORIGINAL SRP	GREENBOOK TRUMKT PRICE
	VARIATIONS/MISC/COLLECTOR NOTES							
SV79-9	MISSION CHURCH	5062-5	Ceramic	NO	✓	RETIRED 1980	$ 30.00	$ 1250.00
	Ceramic bell is attached by wire.							
SV79-10	MOBILE HOME	5063-3	Ceramic	NO	✓	RETIRED 1980	18.00	1750.00
SV79-11	GIANT TREES	5065-8	Ceramic	NO	✓	RETIRED 1982	20.00	360.00
	Approximately 11" tall.							
SV79-12	ADOBE HOUSE	5066-6	Ceramic	NO	✓	RETIRED 1980	18.00	2500.00

CLIPBOARD
- First year of retirement.

SV80-1

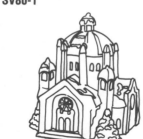

CATHEDRAL CHURCH

Central dome with two shorter bell towers.

SV80-2

STONE MILL HOUSE

Waterwheel on dark weathered stone block mill, bag of grain hangs from block and tackle, another bag propped by door.

SV80-3

COLONIAL FARM HOUSE

Wide front porch, two front dormers in attic, symmetrical layout of windows.

SV80-4

TOWN CHURCH

Short bell tower rises from central nave area, attached tree tucks in close to side chapel.

SV80-5

TRAIN STATION WITH 3 TRAIN CARS

Station clock over entry door, two small wings on either side of main room, brick and timbered design. Train – engine, passenger car, baggage/mail caboose. "G&N RR" on all cars.

ART CHART #	NAME	ITEM #	MATERIAL	SET?	(lightbulb)	MARKET STATUS	ORIGINAL SRP	GREENBOOK TRUMKT PRICE
	VARIATIONS/MISC/COLLECTOR NOTES							
SV80-1	CATHEDRAL CHURCH	5067-4	Ceramic*	NO	✓	RETIRED 1981	$ 36.00	$ 2000.00
	Production problems (fragile domes) forced retirement after one year. *Stained glass windows are acrylic. Inspired by St. Paul's Cathedral in St. Paul, MN.							
SV80-2	STONE MILL HOUSE	5068-2	Ceramic	NO	✓	RETIRED 1982	30.00	495.00
	Separate bag of oats hung with wire.							
SV80-3	COLONIAL FARM HOUSE	5070-9	Ceramic	NO	✓	RETIRED 1982	30.00	375.00
SV80-4	TOWN CHURCH	5071-7	Ceramic	NO	✓	RETIRED 1982	33.00	375.00
	Same Item # was used for the 1986 Carriage House (SV86-12).							
SV80-5	TRAIN STATION WITH 3 TRAIN CARS	5085-6	Ceramic	SET OF 4	✓	RETIRED 1985	100.00	See Below
	Variation: Original station, smaller in size and had 6 window panes, round window in door. Brick on front, not sides - Market Price $395. Revised had 8 window panes, 2 square windows in door, brick on front and sides - Market Price $325. First Original Snow Village train and station design. All four pieces lit.							

CLIPBOARD

- Few introductions due to large number of ongoing pieces.
- Understamping accompanied adhesive stickers.

1981 THE ORIGINAL SNOW VILLAGE 1981

SV81-1

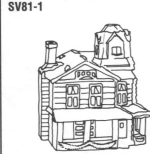

WOODEN CLAPBOARD

White house with green roof and trim and wraparound porch. Red brick chimney.

SV81-2

ENGLISH COTTAGE

Thatched roof and timbered frame, two chimneys. 1-1/2 stories. Roof comes down to meet top of first story.

SV81-3

BARN

Red barn and silo. Grey roof, two vents on roof ridge, root cellar on side, hay loft over animals and equipment.

SV81-4

CORNER STORE

Red brick with one large display window, entry door on corner, bay window in family living area, shutters on windows, shingled roof.

SV81-5

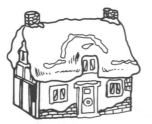

BAKERY

Bakery store beneath family living area, white with green trim, half turret form gives unique angle to front and second story bay window.

SV81-6

ENGLISH CHURCH

Steep pitched roof, side chapel, steeple topped by gold cross, arched windows, triangular window in gable above entry double doors.

SV81-7

LARGE SINGLE TREE

One snow covered evergreen tree. Birds perch on branches.

ART CHART #	NAME	ITEM #	MATERIAL	SET?	!	MARKET STATUS	ORIGINAL SRP	GREENBOOK TRUMKT PRICE
	VARIATIONS/MISC/COLLECTOR NOTES							
SV81-1	WOODEN CLAPBOARD	5072-5	Ceramic	NO	✓	RETIRED 1984	$ 32.00	$ 260.00
SV81-2	ENGLISH COTTAGE	5073-3	Ceramic	NO	✓	RETIRED 1982	25.00	295.00
	Variations in color of thatched roof.							
SV81-3	BARN	5074-1	Ceramic	NO	✓	RETIRED 1984	32.00	460.00
	aka "Original Barn."							
SV81-4	CORNER STORE	5076-8	Ceramic	NO	✓	RETIRED 1983	30.00	245.00
	Same Item # was used for the 1986 Apothecary (SV86-14).							
SV81-5	BAKERY	5077-6	Ceramic	NO	✓	RETIRED 1983	30.00	250.00
	This is the original Bakery. Same Item # was used for the 1986 Bakery – a new and different design. Designed after The Scofield Building in Northfield, MN.							
SV81-6	ENGLISH CHURCH	5078-4	Ceramic	NO	✓	RETIRED 1982	30.00	395.00
	The Cross is separate and inserts into the steeple. Same Item # was used for the 1986 Diner (SV86-16).							
SV81-7	LARGE SINGLE TREE	5080-6	Ceramic	NO	✓	RETIRED 1989	17.00	45.00
	Mold changes and variations in amount of snow over the years. Approximately 9" tall.							

1982 . . . THE ORIGINAL SNOW VILLAGE 1982 . . .

SV82-1

SKATING POND

Snowman on edge of small snow covered skating pond. Tree trunks piled together provide seating. Two evergreen trees complete the set.

SV82-2

STREET CAR

Bright yellow with green "Main Street" sign on side. #2 car, hook-up on top for pole to connect to electric power.

SV82-3

CENTENNIAL HOUSE

Two story clapboard, square tower, carved and curved window frames, "wooden" balcony & porch.

SV82-4

CARRIAGE HOUSE

Bright lamps flank entry to storage area for carriages. Driver has small apartment above.

SV82-5

PIONEER CHURCH

Simple design appears to be of wood construction, front notice board sends joy to all who pass, short steeple on front of roof ridge.

SV82-6

SWISS CHALET

Stone base walls support timber upper stories. Upper floor has front balcony with railing and is enclosed by roof overhang. Unusual roof.

SV82-7

BANK

Corner building with entry by revolving door. Outside covered stairway leads to second story. Sign becomes part of corner design.

SV82-8

GABLED HOUSE

Shingled house with four gabled roof, two small covered porches, one lower and one upper window to each side.

ART CHART #	NAME	ITEM #	MATERIAL	SET?	!	MARKET STATUS	ORIGINAL SRP	GREENBOOK TRUMKT PRICE
	VARIATIONS/MISC/COLLECTOR NOTES							
SV82-1	SKATING POND	5017-2	Ceramic	SET OF 2	✓	RETIRED 1984	$ 25.00	$ 380.00
	Replaces the Skating Rink/Duck Pond Set, 1978, #5015-3, (SV78-5). Has two trees. Trees are separate from the pond.							
SV82-2	STREET CAR	5019-9	Ceramic	NO	✓	RETIRED 1984	16.00	395.00
SV82-3	CENTENNIAL HOUSE	5020-2	Ceramic	NO	✓	RETIRED 1984	32.00	350.00
SV82-4	CARRIAGE HOUSE	5021-0	Ceramic	NO	✓	RETIRED 1984	28.00	325.00
SV82-5	PIONEER CHURCH	5022-9	Ceramic	NO	✓	RETIRED 1984	30.00	300.00
SV82-6	SWISS CHALET	5023-7	Ceramic	NO	✓	RETIRED 1984	28.00	450.00
SV82-7	BANK	5024-5	Ceramic	NO	✓	RETIRED 1983	32.00	600.00
	Same Item # was used for the 1987 Cumberland House (SV87-4).							
SV82-8	GABLED HOUSE	5081-4	Ceramic	NO	✓	RETIRED 1983	30.00	390.00
	Variations in color. Same Item # was used for the 1987 Red Barn (SV87-7). Early release to Gift Creations Concepts.							

SV82-9

FLOWER SHOP

Flower boxes rest outside by large display window. Rolled up awnings above front windows.

SV82-10

NEW STONE CHURCH

Long nave with side chapel, stone block construction, steeple rises on side opposite chapel. Front has arched windows and two lamps.

ART CHART #	NAME	ITEM #	MATERIAL	SET?	💡	MARKET STATUS	ORIGINAL SRP	GREENBOOK TRUMKT PRICE
	VARIATIONS/MISC/COLLECTOR NOTES							
SV82-9	FLOWER SHOP	5082-2	Ceramic	NO	✓	RETIRED 1983	$ 25.00	$ 450.00
	Variations in color. Same Item # was used for the 1987 Jefferson School (SV87-8).							
SV82-10	NEW STONE CHURCH	5083-0	Ceramic	NO	✓	RETIRED 1984	32.00	395.00
	Early release to Gift Creations Concepts.							

1983 . . . THE ORIGINAL SNOW VILLAGE 1983 . . .

SV83-1

TOWN HALL

Brick and stone, two corner covered side entries, symmetrical design (window over window), steeple above front main wall.

SV83-2

GROCERY

Red brick, full painted display windows, decorative cornice trim above/below front windows. Outside staircase leads to family quarters.

SV83-3

VICTORIAN COTTAGE

Ornate carved woodwork on house front, ornamental arched entry design. First floor French windows separated by pillars.

SV83-4

GOVERNOR'S MANSION

Brick, metal ironwork featured on roof cupola, wide entry steps, repetitive design above door, second story, and central attic windows.

SV83-5

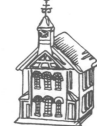

TURN OF THE CENTURY

Steps lead to covered entry, front triangular ornate design crowns front gable, squared turret rises from left front corner and ends in highest roof peak.

SV83-6

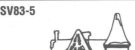

GINGERBREAD HOUSE

Designed like a Christmas edible treat. Cookies trim sides while candy canes and sugar heart decorate roof.

SV83-7

VILLAGE CHURCH

Stone steps lead to double carved doors, design repeats on roof trim. Steeple has long narrow openings. Pointed arch windows are featured.

SV83-8

GOTHIC CHURCH

Stone block, steeple rises straight from large double doors ending in a cross. Bell chamber has ornate grillwork. Smaller entry doors flank central area repeating design.

ART CHART #	NAME	ITEM #	MATERIAL	SET?	!	MARKET STATUS	ORIGINAL SRP	GREENBOOK TRUMKT PRICE
	VARIATIONS/MISC/COLLECTOR NOTES							
SV83-1	TOWN HALL	5000-8	Ceramic*	NO	✓	RETIRED 1984	$ 32.00	$ 345.00
	Ceramic bell in tower. *Stamped metal weathervane is separate.							
SV83-2	GROCERY	5001-6	Ceramic	NO	✓	RETIRED 1985	35.00	325.00
SV83-3	VICTORIAN COTTAGE	5002-4	Ceramic	NO	✓	RETIRED 1984	35.00	365.00
SV83-4	GOVERNOR'S MANSION	5003-2	Ceramic*	NO	✓	RETIRED 1985	32.00	275.00
	*Metal trim on front tower.							
SV83-5	TURN OF THE CENTURY	5004-0	Ceramic	NO	✓	RETIRED 1986	36.00	235.00
SV83-6	GINGERBREAD HOUSE	5025-3	Ceramic	NO		RETIRED 1984	24.00	270.00
	See footnote[1], page 31.							
SV83-7	VILLAGE CHURCH	5026-1	Ceramic	NO	✓	RETIRED 1984	30.00	375.00
	Early release to Gift Creations Concepts.							
SV83-8	GOTHIC CHURCH	5028-8	Ceramic	NO	✓	RETIRED 1986	36.00	275.00

SV83-9

PARSONAGE

Tower rises above entry. Ornate coping on front gable topped by Cross. Coping details repeated around windows, doors, and small balcony. Community rooms on first floor, family lives upstairs.

SV83-10

WOODEN CHURCH

White clapboard, crossed timber design repeats over door, roof peak, and steeple. Side chapel has separate entry door.

SV83-11

FIRE STATION

Central doors open to reveal red fire truck. Brick columns from base to roof add to sturdy look. Dalmatian sits by entry, ready when necessary.

SV83-12

ENGLISH TUDOR

Stucco finish. Brick chimneys. Three front roof peaks create front gable design.

SV83-13

CHATEAU

First story large windows which include front and side bow windows are a feature. Diamond design on roof shingles, stone for walls, cylindrical chimney with domed flue cap. Front dormers and side peaks exhibit ornate carved design.

ART CHART #	NAME	ITEM #	MATERIAL	SET?	💡	MARKET STATUS	ORIGINAL SRP	GREENBOOK TRUMKT PRICE
	VARIATIONS/MISC/COLLECTOR NOTES							
SV83-9	PARSONAGE	5029-6	Ceramic	NO	✓	RETIRED 1985	$ 35.00	$ 350.00
SV83-10	WOODEN CHURCH	5031-8	Ceramic	NO	✓	RETIRED 1985	30.00	350.00
SV83-11	FIRE STATION	5032-6	Ceramic	NO	✓	RETIRED 1984	32.00	625.00
	Variation: without dog.							
SV83-12	ENGLISH TUDOR	5033-4	Ceramic	NO	✓	RETIRED 1985	30.00	295.00
SV83-13	CHATEAU	5084-9	Ceramic	NO	✓	RETIRED 1984	35.00	475.00
	Early release to Gift Creations Concepts.							

[1] In 1983, Department 56 issued the **Gingerbread House** with all intentions of it being a lit house. After realizing it did not fit well with the other Snow Village Houses, Department 56 decided to close the light hole in the back, put in a slot for coins and create a bank! Some of the original lit pieces made their way to consumers through the Bachman's stores, leading to much of the confusion. Adding to the confusion, is the fact that the Gingerbread House is listed as a Snow Village piece in the SV History List. (Note it does not appear in the 1994 Snow Village poster.)

1984 . . . THE ORIGINAL SNOW VILLAGE 1984 . . .

SV84-1

MAIN STREET HOUSE

White and green 1-1/2 story house. Clapboard lower story with timbered upper story, two lamps outside front door.

SV84-2

STRATFORD HOUSE

Vertical ornamental timbers featured, gables all rise to same height.

SV84-3

HAVERSHAM HOUSE

All gables, balconies, porch, decorated with ornately carved woodwork.

SV84-4

GALENA HOUSE

Steps lead to double entry doors of brick home. Bay window fills one side. Second floor incorporated into roof construction.

SV84-5

RIVER ROAD HOUSE

White house, large and grand with many windows, first floor front windows are highlighted with half circle paned glass above them, side bay windows project out from house wall.

SV84-6

DELTA HOUSE

Brick house with balcony above wrap-around porch which is separate from entry. Porch design is repeated where roof and brick meet and on turret.

SV84-7

BAYPORT

Corner entry with a turret addition positioned between the two main wings of two story house.

SV84-8

CONGREGATIONAL CHURCH

Brick with fieldstone front. Stone repeated on steeple. Louver vents on belfry.

ART CHART #	NAME	ITEM #	MATERIAL	SET?		MARKET STATUS	ORIGINAL SRP	GREENBOOK TRUMKT PRICE
	VARIATIONS/MISC/COLLECTOR NOTES							
SV84-1	MAIN STREET HOUSE	5005-9	Ceramic	NO	✓	RETIRED 1986	$ 27.00	$ 275.00
	Early release to Gift Creations Concepts.							
SV84-2	STRATFORD HOUSE	5007-5	Ceramic	NO	✓	RETIRED 1986	28.00	195.00
SV84-3	HAVERSHAM HOUSE	5008-3	Ceramic	NO	✓	RETIRED 1987	37.00	300.00
	Early release to Gift Creations Concepts. Variations: early release pieces are larger than subsequent ones.							
SV84-4	GALENA HOUSE	5009-1	Ceramic	NO	✓	RETIRED 1985	32.00	345.00
SV84-5	RIVER ROAD HOUSE	5010-5	Ceramic	NO	✓	RETIRED 1987	36.00	215.00
	Early release to Gift Creations Concepts. Variations in window cuts.							
SV84-6	DELTA HOUSE	5012-1	Ceramic*	NO	✓	RETIRED 1986	32.00	310.00
	*"Iron works" atop tower.							
SV84-7	BAYPORT	5015-6	Ceramic	NO	✓	RETIRED 1986	30.00	235.00
SV84-8	CONGREGATIONAL CHURCH	5034-2	Ceramic	NO	✓	RETIRED 1985	28.00	595.00

. . . 1984 THE ORIGINAL SNOW VILLAGE . . . 1984

SV84-9

TRINITY CHURCH

Steeples of different heights, clerestory windows to bring additional light to nave, two large wreaths by front doors.

SV84-10

SUMMIT HOUSE

Corner house features rounded turret, large entry door with side lights, cornices appear to support roof edge. Each second story window capped by a molded projection.

SV84-11

NEW SCHOOL HOUSE

Two story schoolhouse with bell tower and clock.

SV84-12

PARISH CHURCH

White country church with unique three level steeple. Arched windows, red door, circular window over entry.

ART CHART #	NAME	ITEM #	MATERIAL	SET?	💡	MARKET STATUS	ORIGINAL SRP	GREENBOOK TRUMKT PRICE
	VARIATIONS/MISC/COLLECTOR NOTES							
SV84-9	TRINITY CHURCH	5035-0	Ceramic	NO	✓	RETIRED 1986	$ 32.00	$ 305.00
SV84-10	SUMMIT HOUSE	5036-9	Ceramic	NO	✓	RETIRED 1985	28.00	385.00
SV84-11	NEW SCHOOL HOUSE	5037-7	Ceramic*	NO	✓	RETIRED 1986	35.00	275.00
	*Separate flag - wooden pole, paper flag (not shown).							
SV84-12	PARISH CHURCH	5039-3	Ceramic	NO	✓	RETIRED 1986	32.00	370.00

SV85-1

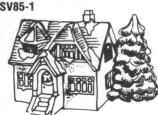

STUCCO BUNGALOW

Two story small house with one roof dormer as mini tower, second dormer features timbered design. Entry door built into archway under a low roof peak. Wreath and garland decorate door.

SV85-2

WILLIAMSBURG HOUSE

Traditional two story colonial, all windows shuttered, three dormers, two chimneys, covered entry topped by second floor balcony.

SV85-3

PLANTATION HOUSE

Entry features two story wood columns, three dormers, two chimneys, four first floor front windows have canopies.

SV85-4

CHURCH OF THE OPEN DOOR

Steeple is on side chapel. Design over front entry above circular window has small repeated motif on eaves.

SV85-5

SPRUCE PLACE

Victorian with windowed turret rising above covered porch. Decorative molding above porch, windows, dormer. Circular window over porch decorated with wreath.

SV85-6

DUPLEX

A two-family house with shared entry. Each family had up/down rooms and a bay window. Design has small second story balcony and roof dormers.

SV85-7

DEPOT AND TRAIN WITH 2 TRAIN CARS

Two wings connected by a central area, each wing has its own chimney, corners of building fortified with stone blocks.

SV85-8

RIDGEWOOD

Porches run length of both first and second story. First floor front windows are arched and design is repeated over front door and on attic windows.

ART CHART #	NAME	ITEM #	MATERIAL	SET?	💡	MARKET STATUS	ORIGINAL SRP	GREENBOOK TRUMKT PRICE
	VARIATIONS/MISC/COLLECTOR NOTES							
SV85-1	STUCCO BUNGALOW	5045-8	Ceramic	NO	✓	RETIRED 1986	$ 30.00	$ 395.00
SV85-2	WILLIAMSBURG HOUSE	5046-6	Ceramic	NO	✓	RETIRED 1988	37.00	135.00
SV85-3	PLANTATION HOUSE	5047-4	Ceramic	NO	✓	RETIRED 1987	37.00	115.00
SV85-4	CHURCH OF THE OPEN DOOR	5048-2	Ceramic	NO	✓	RETIRED 1988	34.00	125.00
SV85-5	SPRUCE PLACE	5049-0	Ceramic	NO	✓	RETIRED 1987	33.00	275.00
SV85-6	DUPLEX	5050-4	Ceramic	NO	✓	RETIRED 1987	35.00	165.00
SV85-7	DEPOT AND TRAIN WITH 2 TRAIN CARS	5051-2	Ceramic	SET OF 4	✓	RETIRED 1988	65.00	145.00
	Train is non-lighting. Variations in color and depot exterior finish. Second Original Snow Village train and station design. Coal car has plastic bag of coal.							
SV85-8	RIDGEWOOD	5052-0	Ceramic	NO	✓	RETIRED 1987	35.00	170.00

1986 . . . THE ORIGINAL SNOW VILLAGE 1986 . . .

SV86-1

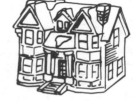

WAVERLY PLACE
Ornate Victorian home has two different turret-like window designs. Second story features half moon window highlights and carved moldings.

SV86-2

TWIN PEAKS
Two matching three story stone turrets, a multitude of windows on each story soften fortress look. Red entry doors reached by wide steps.

SV86-3

2101 MAPLE
Brick two story home. Side of front porch built out from stone turret. Two story bay windows capped by half circle window.

SV86-4

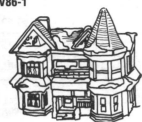

LINCOLN PARK DUPLEX
Two family attached home. Each has two story bay windows and share a front door. Floor plan unique feature is placement of chimneys – as if floor plans reversed, one is at front, other is at rear.

SV86-5

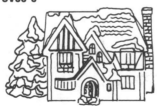

SONOMA HOUSE
Flavor of Southwest. Stucco walls, red roof. Decorative curved front rises up two and a half stories. Square turret adjacent to front door capped by same design which repeats on chimney.

SV86-6

HIGHLAND PARK HOUSE
Brick, timbered, and gabled house brings English Tudor design to cozy home. Rounded arch front door repeats theme in two windows in mid roof gable. Brick chimney on side.

SV86-7

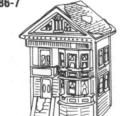

BEACON HILL HOUSE
A row house, typical of urban Boston, MA neighborhoods. Has a solid compact look. Features bay windows on first and second story highlighted by paneled framing.

SV86-8

PACIFIC HEIGHTS HOUSE
A West Coast row house that appears tall and narrow based on repeated vertical theme of front porch/balcony support columns.

ART CHART #	NAME	ITEM #	MATERIAL	SET?	!	MARKET STATUS	ORIGINAL SRP	GREENBOOK TRUMKT PRICE
	VARIATIONS/MISC/COLLECTOR NOTES							
SV86-1	WAVERLY PLACE	5041-5	Ceramic	NO	✓	RETIRED 1986	$ 35.00	$ 325.00
	Early release to Gift Creations Concepts, Fall 1985. Designed after the Gingerbread Mansion in Ferndale, CA.							
SV86-2	TWIN PEAKS	5042-3	Ceramic	NO	✓	RETIRED 1986	32.00	525.00
	Early release to Gift Creations Concepts, Fall 1985.							
SV86-3	2101 MAPLE	5043-1	Ceramic	NO	✓	RETIRED 1986	32.00	375.00
	Early release to Gift Creations Concepts, Fall 1985.							
SV86-4	LINCOLN PARK DUPLEX	5060-1	Ceramic	NO	✓	RETIRED 1988	33.00	125.00
SV86-5	SONOMA HOUSE	5062-8	Ceramic	NO	✓	RETIRED 1988	33.00	120.00
	Early release to Gift Creations Concepts, Fall 1986.							
SV86-6	HIGHLAND PARK HOUSE	5063-6	Ceramic	NO	✓	RETIRED 1988	35.00	150.00
	Early release to Gift Creations Concepts, Fall 1986.							
SV86-7	BEACON HILL HOUSE	5065-2	Ceramic	NO	✓	RETIRED 1988	31.00	150.00
SV86-8	PACIFIC HEIGHTS HOUSE	5066-0	Ceramic	NO	✓	RETIRED 1988	33.00	100.00

. . . 1986 THE ORIGINAL SNOW VILLAGE . . . 1986

SV86-9

RAMSEY HILL HOUSE

Victorian with double chimneys. Steps to front door, porch is adjacent to entry. Side door also features small porch. Low balustrade fronts second story windows. Handpainting adds detailing to design.

SV86-10

SAINT JAMES CHURCH

Long central nave flanked by lower roofed side sections fronted by two towers. Gold main cross reinforced by smaller crosses on each section of tower roof. Smaller round windows repeat central window.

SV86-11

ALL SAINTS CHURCH

Smaller country church, simple design of long nave with entry door in base of bell tower.

SV86-12

CARRIAGE HOUSE

Small home from building used originally for carriages. A second story is achieved with many dormer windows. Fieldstone makes up the foundation allowing great weight during original function.

SV86-13

TOY SHOP

Front windows display toys. Roof molding brings focus to teddy bear design under pediment. Three story brick.

SV86-14

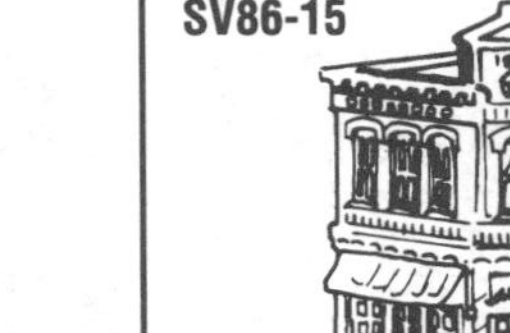

APOTHECARY

Two doors flank a central display bow window. Mortar & pestle symbolizes the profession of owner and is on front panel above second floor family windows.

SV86-15

BAKERY

Corner bakery with two large multi-paned display windows protected by ribbed canopy. Greek key designs around roof edging highlight the bas-relief cupcake topped by a cherry that is centrally placed over entry.

SV86-16

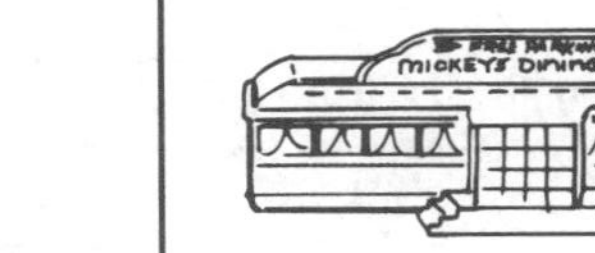

DINER

An eating place based on the railroads famous dining car. Reputation of good, wholesome food. Large windows are a feature. Glass block entry protects diners from weather as customers come in/go out. Diners generally have counter service as well as a dining room.

ART CHART #	NAME	ITEM #	MATERIAL	SET?	!	MARKET STATUS	ORIGINAL SRP	GREENBOOK TRUMKT PRICE
	VARIATIONS/MISC/COLLECTOR NOTES							
SV86-9	RAMSEY HILL HOUSE	5067-9	Ceramic	NO	✓	RETIRED 1989	$ 36.00	$ 95.00
	Early release to Gift Creations Concepts, Fall 1986.							
SV86-10	SAINT JAMES CHURCH	5068-7	Ceramic	NO	✓	RETIRED 1988	37.00	175.00
SV86-11	ALL SAINTS CHURCH	5070-9	Ceramic	NO	✓	CURRENT	38.00	45.00
SV86-12	CARRIAGE HOUSE	5071-7	Ceramic	NO	✓	RETIRED 1988	29.00	110.00
	Same Item # was used for the 1980 Town Church (SV80-4).							
SV86-13	TOY SHOP	5073-3	Ceramic	NO	✓	RETIRED 1990	36.00	90.00
	Main Street design. Design is based on the Finch Building in Hastings, Minnesota.							
SV86-14	APOTHECARY	5076-8	Ceramic	NO	✓	RETIRED 1990	34.00	90.00
	Main Street design. Based on Hasting, MN's former City Hall. Some sleeves read "Antique Shop." Same Item # was used for the 1981 Corner Store (SV81-4).							
SV86-15	BAKERY	5077-6	Ceramic	NO	✓	RETIRED 1991	35.00	85.00
	Main Street design. Designed after Scofield Building in Northfield, MN. Same Item # was used for first SV Bakery: 1981 Bakery (SV81-5).							
SV86-16	DINER	5078-4	Ceramic	NO	✓	RETIRED 1987	22.00	550.00
	Also known as "Mickey's." Designed after Mickey's Diner in St. Paul, MN. Same Item # was used for the 1981 English Church (SV81-6).							

1987 . . . THE ORIGINAL SNOW VILLAGE 1987 . . .

SV87-1

ST. ANTHONY HOTEL & POST OFFICE

Three story red brick with green trim. Dated 1886, the address of this hotel is "56 Main Street." American flag flies outside the ground floor P.O.

SV87-2

SNOW VILLAGE FACTORY

Wood building rises on stone block base with tall smokestack at rear. Factory products were available in small shop at front.

SV87-3

CATHEDRAL

Mosaic "stained glass" decorates the Gothic windows on all sides as well as the large turret.

SV87-4

CUMBERLAND HOUSE

Multi-colored curved roof supported by four columns, two chimneys, shuttered windows.

SV87-5

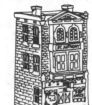

SPRINGFIELD HOUSE

Lower level has two multi-paned bay windows, one is bowed. Upper level windows are shuttered. Roof dormers are half-circle sunbursts. Stone chimney completes this clapboard home.

SV87-6

LIGHTHOUSE

Five story lighthouse beacon rises from sturdy stone slab base and is connected to caretaker's cottage.

SV87-7

RED BARN

Stone base, wooden barn, double cross-buck doors on long side, hayloft doors above main doors. Three ventilator cupolas on roof ridge. Cat sleeps in hayloft.

SV87-8

JEFFERSON SCHOOL

Two room schoolhouse with large multi-paned windows with top transoms. Short bell tower incorporated into roof.

ART CHART #	NAME	ITEM #	MATERIAL	SET?	!	MARKET STATUS	ORIGINAL SRP	GREENBOOK TRUMKT PRICE
	VARIATIONS/MISC/COLLECTOR NOTES							
SV87-1	ST. ANTHONY HOTEL & POST OFFICE	5006-7	Ceramic*	NO	✓	RETIRED 1989	$ 40.00	$ 110.00
	Main Street addition. *Metal flag.							
SV87-2	SNOW VILLAGE FACTORY	5013-0	Ceramic	SET OF 2	✓	RETIRED 1989	45.00	120.00
	Smoke stack is separate.							
SV87-3	CATHEDRAL	5019-9	Ceramic	NO	✓	RETIRED 1990	50.00	100.00
SV87-4	CUMBERLAND HOUSE	5024-5	Ceramic	NO	✓	CURRENT	42.00	45.00
	Same Item # was used for the 1982 Bank (SV82-7).							
SV87-5	SPRINGFIELD HOUSE	5027-0	Ceramic	NO	✓	RETIRED 1990	40.00	75.00
SV87-6	LIGHTHOUSE	5030-0	Ceramic	NO	✓	RETIRED 1988	36.00	595.00
	Variation: glazed and unglazed.							
SV87-7	RED BARN	5081-4	Ceramic	NO	✓	RETIRED 1992	38.00	75.00
	Same Item # was used for the 1982 Gabled House (SV82-8). Early release to Gift Creations Concepts.							
SV87-8	JEFFERSON SCHOOL	5082-2	Ceramic	NO	✓	RETIRED 1991	36.00	145.00
	Same Item # was used for the 1982 Flower Shop (SV82-9). Early release to Gift Creations Concepts.							

SV87-9

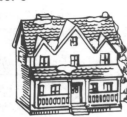

FARM HOUSE

2-1/2 story wood frame home with front full-length porch. Roof interest is two low, one high peak with attic window in highest peak.

SV87-10

FIRE STATION NO. 2

Large double doors for station housing two engines, side stair leads to living quarters. Brick building with stone arch design at engine doors and front windows.

SV87-11

SNOW VILLAGE RESORT LODGE

Bright yellow with green, scalloped roof, covered porch and side entry. Bay windows on front house section. Back section rises to dormered 3-1/2 stories. Ventilator areas directly under roof cap.

ART CHART #	NAME	ITEM #	MATERIAL	SET?	!	MARKET STATUS	ORIGINAL SRP	GREENBOOK TRUMKT PRICE
	VARIATIONS/MISC/COLLECTOR NOTES							
SV87-9	FARM HOUSE	5089-0	Ceramic	NO	✓	RETIRED 1992	$ 40.00	$ 65.00
SV87-10	FIRE STATION NO. 2	5091-1	Ceramic	NO	✓	RETIRED 1989	40.00	185.00
	Early release to Gift Creations Concepts.							
SV87-11	SNOW VILLAGE RESORT LODGE	5092-0	Ceramic	NO	✓	RETIRED 1989	55.00	140.00

1988 . . . THE ORIGINAL SNOW VILLAGE 1988 . . .

SV88-1

VILLAGE MARKET

Silk-screened "glass" windows detail merchandise available, red and white canopy protects shoppers using in/out doors. Sign over second story windows.

SV88-2

KENWOOD HOUSE

Old-fashioned wrap-around veranda with arched openings on three story home. Front facade features scalloped shingles on third story.

SV88-3

MAPLE RIDGE INN

Replica of Victorian mansion, ornamental roof piece concealed lightning rods.

SV88-4

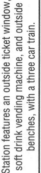

VILLAGE STATION AND TRAIN

Station features an outside ticket window, soft drink vending machine, and outside benches, with a three car train.

SV88-5

COBBLESTONE ANTIQUE SHOP

Silk-screened front windows display antiques for sale, bay window fills second story width, building date of 1881 on arched cornice.

SV88-6

CORNER CAFE

"Pie" and "Coffee" silkscreen on windows of corner restaurant with red, white, and blue striped awnings. Building date of 1875 inscribed on turret design.

SV88-7

SINGLE CAR GARAGE

Double doors open to house car, two outside lights for convenience, designed to look like house, windows have shutters, roof has dormers, roof projects over wood pile.

SV88-8

HOME SWEET HOME/ HOUSE & WINDMILL

Based on landmark historic home, saltbox with asymmetrical arrangement of windows. Doors for root cellar are at front corner, one central brick chimney. Four bladed windmill.

ART CHART #	NAME	ITEM #	MATERIAL	SET?	💡	MARKET STATUS	ORIGINAL SRP	GREENBOOK TRUMKT PRICE
	VARIATIONS/MISC/COLLECTOR NOTES							
SV88-1	VILLAGE MARKET	5044-0	Ceramic	NO	✓	RETIRED 1991	$ 39.00	$ 65.00
	Early release to Gift Creations Concepts.							
SV88-2	KENWOOD HOUSE	5054-7	Ceramic	NO	✓	RETIRED 1990	50.00	125.00
	Early release to Gift Creations Concepts.							
SV88-3	MAPLE RIDGE INN	5121-7	Ceramic	NO	✓	RETIRED 1990	55.00	65.00
	Interpretation of an American landmark in Cambridge, New York. 1991 GCC Catalog Exclusive @ $75.00.							
SV88-4	VILLAGE STATION AND TRAIN	5122-5	Ceramic	SET OF 4	✓	RETIRED 1992	65.00	100.00
	Third Original Snow Village train and station design. Train cars do not light.							
SV88-5	COBBLESTONE ANTIQUE SHOP	5123-3	Ceramic	NO	✓	RETIRED 1992	36.00	65.00
SV88-6	CORNER CAFE	5124-1	Ceramic	NO	✓	RETIRED 1991	37.00	90.00
SV88-7	SINGLE CAR GARAGE	5125-0	Ceramic	NO	✓	RETIRED 1990	22.00	50.00
SV88-8	HOME SWEET HOME/HOUSE & WINDMILL	5126-8	Ceramic*	SET OF 2	✓	RETIRED 1991	60.00	115.00
	* Metal blades of windmill are separate. Inspired by the home of John Howard Payne, composer of "Home Sweet Home," in East Hampton, New York.							

SV88-9	SV88-10	SV88-11	SV88-12
 **REDEEMER CHURCH** Stone corners add strength and support to church and bell tower. Arched windows, heavy wooden double doors.	 **SERVICE STATION** Two gas pumps, candy machine, restroom, work area and office. White building, blue roof, red trim.	 **STONEHURST HOUSE** Red brick punctuated with black and white painted bricks. Half circle sunburst design second story dormers restate the arch shape of first floor windows.	 **PALOS VERDES** Spanish style with green tiled roof, covered entry porch, stucco finish, 2nd floor has shuttered windows. Coming forward from main wing is 2 story round turret and ground floor window alcove.

ART CHART #	NAME	ITEM #	MATERIAL	SET?	💡	MARKET STATUS	ORIGINAL SRP	GREENBOOK TRUMKT PRICE
	VARIATIONS/MISC/COLLECTOR NOTES							
SV88-9	REDEEMER CHURCH	5127-6	Ceramic	NO	✓	RETIRED 1992	$ 42.00	$ 60.00
SV88-10	SERVICE STATION	5128-4	Ceramic	SET OF 2	✓	RETIRED 1991	37.50	295.00
	aka "Bill's Service Station." Pumps included. Pumps do not light.							
SV88-11	STONEHURST HOUSE	5140-3	Ceramic	NO	✓	RETIRED 1994	37.50	60.00
SV88-12	PALOS VERDES	5141-1	Ceramic*	NO	✓	RETIRED 1990	37.50	80.00
	*Potted sisal miniature tree on porch - separate.							

SV89-1

JINGLE BELLE HOUSEBOAT

Floating house sports a Christmas tree on wheelhouse roof and rear deck. Name is stenciled on bow and life preservers. Gray, blue, offset by red trim and white rails.

SV89-2

COLONIAL CHURCH

Front entry with four floor to roof columns supporting roof over porch. Front facade repeats design with four half columns set into wall. Cross on three tier steeple bell tower.

SV89-3

NORTH CREEK COTTAGE

Cape cod style with colonial columned front porch. Attached garage with deck on top, front dormer, stone chimney.

SV89-4

PARAMOUNT THEATER

Spanish theme Art Deco building, double marques. Ticket booth in center flanked by two double doors. Corner billboards display scenes from movie.

SV89-5

DOCTOR'S HOUSE

Home and office within house. Rounded turret completes front. Three story home has arched, porthole, and bay windows to add to Victorian charm.

SV89-6

COURTHOUSE

Four corner roof turrets with central clock tower, windows with half circle sunbursts, decorative molding on second story with two front windows being clear half-circles.

SV89-7

VILLAGE WARMING HOUSE

Used by skaters to warm up from the chill, small red house has steep front roof. Bench at side for a brief rest.

SV89-8

J. YOUNG'S GRANARY

Central waterwheel for grinding grain, stone silo on one side, and small storage/store on other side.

ART CHART #	NAME	ITEM #	MATERIAL	SET?	!	MARKET STATUS	ORIGINAL SRP	GREENBOOK TRUMKT PRICE
	VARIATIONS/MISC/COLLECTOR NOTES							
SV89-1	JINGLE BELLE HOUSEBOAT	5114-4	Ceramic*	NO	✓	RETIRED 1991	$ 42.00	$ 100.00
	*Stamped metal bell is separate.							
SV89-2	COLONIAL CHURCH	5119-5	Ceramic*	NO	✓	RETIRED 1992	60.00	75.00
	Early release to Gift Creations Concepts. *Metal cross.							
SV89-3	NORTH CREEK COTTAGE	5120-9	Ceramic	NO	✓	RETIRED 1992	45.00	55.00
	Early release to Gift Creations Concepts.							
SV89-4	PARAMOUNT THEATER	5142-0	Ceramic	NO	✓	RETIRED 1993	42.00	85.00
SV89-5	DOCTOR'S HOUSE	5143-8	Ceramic	NO	✓	RETIRED 1992	56.00	95.00
SV89-6	COURTHOUSE	5144-6	Ceramic	NO	✓	RETIRED 1993	65.00	125.00
	Design based on Gibson County Courthouse in Princeton, IN.							
SV89-7	VILLAGE WARMING HOUSE	5145-4	Ceramic	NO	✓	RETIRED 1992	42.00	60.00
	Trees detach.							
SV89-8	J. YOUNG'S GRANARY	5149-7	Ceramic	NO	✓	RETIRED 1992	45.00	65.00

SV89-9

PINEWOOD LOG CABIN

Log construction with two fireplaces for heating/cooking, tree trunk porch pillars, firewood stack, red roof, house name on sign above porch, attached tree.

ART CHART #	NAME	ITEM #	MATERIAL	SET?	💡	MARKET STATUS	ORIGINAL SRP	GREENBOOK TRUMKT PRICE
	VARIATIONS/MISC/COLLECTOR NOTES							
SV89-9	PINEWOOD LOG CABIN	5150-0	Ceramic	NO	✓	CURRENT	$ 37.50	$ 37.50
	Early release to Gift Creations Concepts, Fall 1990.							

SV90-1

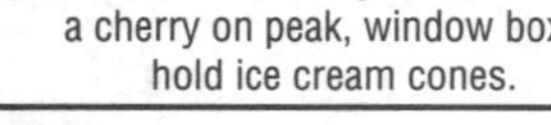

56 FLAVORS ICE CREAM PARLOR

Decorated like a sundae, peppermint pillars flank door, sugar cone roof with a cherry on peak, window boxes hold ice cream cones.

SV90-2

MORNINGSIDE HOUSE

Pink/coral split level house with one car garage. Fieldstone chimney, curved front steps, terraced landscaping with movable trees.

SV90-3

MAINSTREET HARDWARE STORE

Three story building with store on ground level. Rental rooms on second and third story with access by outside staircase. Awning covers display window.

SV90-4

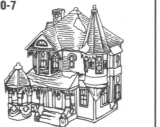

VILLAGE REALTY

Two story main building houses real estate office. Front bay display window for available properties. Adjacent building houses small Italian dining place with colorful striped awning.

SV90-5

SPANISH MISSION CHURCH

Sun dried clay Spanish style, arcade along one side gives protected access.

SV90-6

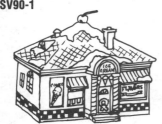

PRAIRIE HOUSE

Two story home with upper floor set in and back atop first story. Large chimney rises up through first story. Two large pillars support covered entry.

SV90-7

QUEEN ANNE VICTORIAN

Broad steps lead up to pillared porch with unique corner gazebo style sitting area. Ornate turret on corner of second story decorated with scalloped shingles.

ART CHART #	NAME	ITEM #	MATERIAL	SET?	!	MARKET STATUS	ORIGINAL SRP	GREENBOOK TRUMKT PRICE
	VARIATIONS/MISC/COLLECTOR NOTES							
SV90-1	56 FLAVORS ICE CREAM PARLOR	5151-9	Ceramic	NO	✓	RETIRED 1992	$ 42.00	$ 80.00
	Early release to Gift Creations Concepts.							
SV90-2	MORNINGSIDE HOUSE	5152-7	Ceramic*	NO	✓	RETIRED 1992	45.00	50.00
	Early release to Showcase Dealers and the National Association of Limited Edition Dealers. *Sisal trees detach.							
SV90-3	MAINSTREET HARDWARE STORE	5153-5	Ceramic	NO	✓	RETIRED 1993	42.00	65.00
	Was originally designed with blue window trim.							
SV90-4	VILLAGE REALTY	5154-3	Ceramic	NO	✓	RETIRED 1993	42.00	70.00
	"J. Saraceno" over door is a tribute to D56's former National Sales Manager.							
SV90-5	SPANISH MISSION CHURCH	5155-1	Ceramic*	NO	✓	RETIRED 1992	42.00	60.00
	*Three metal crosses for cemetery. Designed after Enga Memorial Chapel in Minneapolis, MN.							
SV90-6	PRAIRIE HOUSE	5156-0	Ceramic	NO	✓	RETIRED 1993	42.00	60.00
	American Architecture Series.							
SV90-7	QUEEN ANNE VICTORIAN	5157-8	Ceramic	NO	✓	CURRENT	48.00	50.00
	American Architecture Series.							

SV91-1

THE CHRISTMAS SHOP

Pediment on brick building advertises the holiday by the French "NOEL." Large Teddy Bear by front window.

SV91-2

OAK GROVE TUDOR

Red brick base with stucco and timbered second story. Fireplace of brick and stone by entry door. Rough stone frames door. Bay window with flower boxes.

SV91-3

THE HONEYMOONER MOTEL

Moon and stars sign above office door is advertisement for motel. White building with blue awnings & doors. Soda and ice machine by office door.

SV91-4

VILLAGE GREENHOUSE

Plant growing area has bricked bottom and "glass" roof to allow sunlight in. Attached small store sells accessories. It has brick chimney, shingled roof, and covered entry.

SV91-5

SOUTHERN COLONIAL

Four columns rise from ground to roof with second story veranda across front. Double chimneys surrounded by a balustrade. Shutters by each window both decorate and shut out heat of sun. Two urns flank steps of entryway.

SV91-6

GOTHIC FARMHOUSE

Columned front porch and entry. First floor large bay window with second story rising to a gable with carved molding which is repeated on two dormer windows over porch. Clapboard home with roof shingles in diamond pattern.

ART CHART #	NAME	ITEM #	MATERIAL	SET?	!	MARKET STATUS	ORIGINAL SRP	GREENBOOK TRUMKT PRICE
	VARIATIONS/MISC/COLLECTOR NOTES							
SV91-1	THE CHRISTMAS SHOP	5097-0	Ceramic	NO	✓	CURRENT	$ 37.50	$ 37.50
	Early release to Gift Creations Concepts and Showcase Dealers.							
SV91-2	OAK GROVE TUDOR	5400-3	Ceramic	NO	✓	RETIRED 1994	42.00	60.00
	Early release to Showcase Dealers.							
SV91-3	THE HONEYMOONER MOTEL	5401-1	Ceramic	NO	✓	RETIRED 1993	42.00	70.00
	Early release to Showcase Dealers.							
SV91-4	VILLAGE GREENHOUSE	5402-0	Ceramic*	NO	✓	CURRENT	35.00	36.00
	*Acrylic panels.							
SV91-5	SOUTHERN COLONIAL	5403-8	Ceramic*	NO	✓	RETIRED 1994	48.00	65.00
	American Architecture Series. *Sisal trees detach.							
SV91-6	GOTHIC FARMHOUSE	5404-6	Ceramic	NO	✓	CURRENT	48.00	48.00
	American Architecture Series.							

SV91-7

FINKLEA'S FINERY COSTUME SHOP

Pediment over front door repeated in roof design. Red awnings over 1st floor display windows. Dressed stone trims the facade of the three story brick building. Hood projects over third floor windows - an area used by piano teacher. Attached side setback is two stories w/ decorated rental return door and awning on upper window.

SV91-8

JACK'S CORNER BARBER SHOP

Also houses M. Schmitt Photography Studio and second floor Tailor Shop. Two story turret separates two identical wings of brick building. Fantail window design repeated on doors and on roof peaks.

SV91-9

DOUBLE BUNGALOW

Early two family home - double entry doors, each side has bow window downstairs, a roof dormer, and own chimney. A brick facade dresses up clapboard house.

ART CHART #	NAME	ITEM #	MATERIAL	SET?	!	MARKET STATUS	ORIGINAL SRP	GREENBOOK TRUMKT PRICE
	VARIATIONS/MISC/COLLECTOR NOTES							
SV91-7	FINKLEA'S FINERY COSTUME SHOP	5405-4	Ceramic	NO	✓	RETIRED 1993	$ 45.00	$ 55.00
SV91-8	JACK'S CORNER BARBER SHOP	5406-2	Ceramic	NO	✓	RETIRED 1994	42.00	55.00
	"M. Schmitt Studio" is in honor of Matthew Schmitt, the photographer for D56's Quarterly, brochures, etc.							
SV91-9	DOUBLE BUNGALOW	5407-0	Ceramic	NO	✓	RETIRED 1994	45.00	55.00

SV92-1

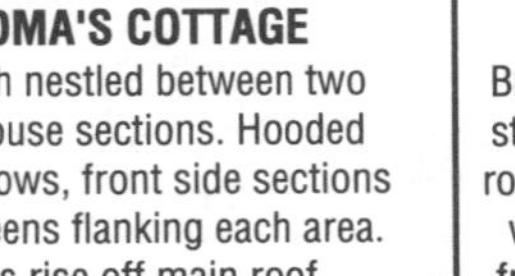

GRANDMA'S COTTAGE

Small porch nestled between two identical house sections. Hooded double windows, front side sections with evergreens flanking each area. Chimneys rise off main roof.

SV92-2

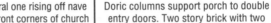

ST. LUKE'S CHURCH

Brick church features three square based steeples w/the central one rising off nave roof. Others are at front corners of church w/doors at base & trefoil design on the front/side repeated on main entry doors.

SV92-3

VILLAGE POST OFFICE

Doric columns support porch to double entry doors. Two story brick with two story turret rising above sign. Greek key and incised design separate stories.

SV92-4

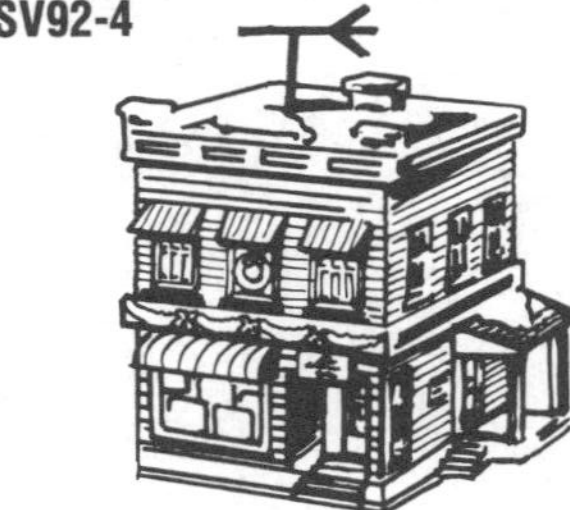

AL'S TV SHOP

TV antenna on roof. Red awnings on upper windows and red canopy over lower display window. Store entry on corner of building.

SV92-5

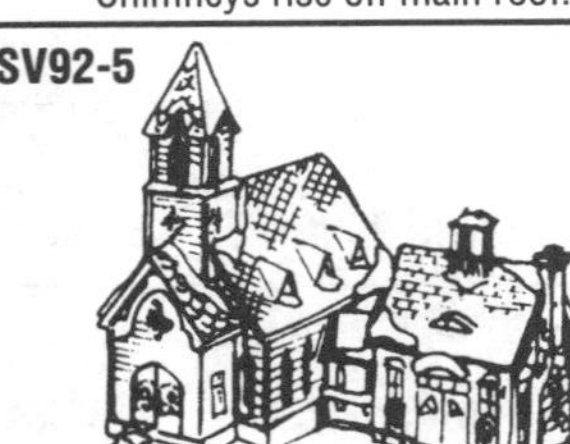

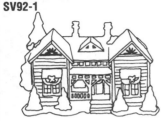

GOOD SHEPHERD CHAPEL & CHURCH SCHOOL

White chapel w/red roof rises on stone base. Steeple at front entry. School has double doors w/tall windows and small bell tower. Stone chimney on side. Church side door meets school side door.

SV92-6

PRINT SHOP & VILLAGE NEWS

Stone in front pediment notes 1893 construction. Symmetrical building design emphasized by double chimneys, matching windows, and columns. Brick building also houses Muffin Shop.

SV92-7

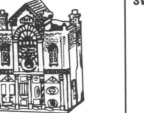

HARTFORD HOUSE

Steeply pitched roof with ornate front covered entry pediment design, repeated in steep front gable. Molding surrounds windows, is present on porch columns.

SV92-8

VILLAGE VET AND PET SHOP

Arched crescents over picture windows that are screened designs depicting dogs, kittens, fish, and birds. Ornamental molding outlines roof edge. Dog sits on entry steps to Vet's office.

ART CHART #	NAME	ITEM #	MATERIAL	SET?	💡	MARKET STATUS	ORIGINAL SRP	GREENBOOK TRUMKT PRICE
	VARIATIONS/MISC/COLLECTOR NOTES							
SV92-1	GRANDMA'S COTTAGE	5420-8	Ceramic	NO	✓	CURRENT	$ 42.00	$ 45.00
	Early release to Gift Creations Concepts.							
SV92-2	ST. LUKE'S CHURCH	5421-6	Ceramic	NO	✓	RETIRED 1994	45.00	60.00
	Early release to Gift Creations Concepts.							
SV92-3	VILLAGE POST OFFICE	5422-4	Ceramic	NO	✓	CURRENT	35.00	37.50
	Early release to Showcase Dealers.							
SV92-4	AL'S TV SHOP	5423-2	Ceramic	NO	✓	CURRENT	40.00	40.00
SV92-5	GOOD SHEPHERD CHAPEL & CHURCH SCHOOL	5424-0	Ceramic	SET OF 2	✓	CURRENT	72.00	72.00
SV92-6	PRINT SHOP & VILLAGE NEWS	5425-9	Ceramic	NO	✓	RETIRED 1994	37.50	55.00
SV92-7	HARTFORD HOUSE	5426-7	Ceramic	NO	✓	CURRENT	55.00	55.00
SV92-8	VILLAGE VET AND PET SHOP	5427-5	Ceramic	NO	✓	CURRENT	32.00	32.00

SV92-9

CRAFTSMAN COTTAGE

Stone based porch extends across front of house ending in stone chimney.
Large squared pillars are part of support for second story room above entryway.
Small dormer by chimney.

SV92-10

VILLAGE STATION

Clock tower rises on one side of two story red brick station.
Platform sign behind a stack of luggage announces arrivals and departures.
Many windowed waiting room for travelers extends length of station.

SV92-11

AIRPORT

Semicircular vaulted roof extends length of plane hangar,
with control tower rising off central rear of building.
One engine prop plane sits in hangar entrance.
Fuel tank pump at corner, plus thermometer, and crop dusting schedule.
Door at opposite front corner for passenger and freight business.

ART CHART #	NAME	ITEM #	MATERIAL	SET?	!	MARKET STATUS	ORIGINAL SRP	GREENBOOK TRUMKT PRICE
	VARIATIONS/MISC/COLLECTOR NOTES							
SV92-9	CRAFTSMAN COTTAGE	5437-2	Ceramic	NO	✓	CURRENT	$ 55.00	$ 55.00
	American Architecture Series.							
SV92-10	VILLAGE STATION	5438-0	Ceramic	NO	✓	CURRENT	65.00	65.00
SV92-11	AIRPORT	5439-9	Ceramic	NO	✓	CURRENT	60.00	60.00

SV93-1

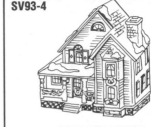

NANTUCKET RENOVATION

Matching gabled wing has been added to the original design & greenhouse has been moved to front of house. Front porch columns are now milled. Small evergreens now at front & large tree moved to rear corner, exposing side bay window.

SV93-2

MOUNT OLIVET CHURCH

Brick church with large stained glass window above double door entry. Square bell tower with steeple roof.

SV93-3

VILLAGE PUBLIC LIBRARY

Brick and stone building with four Greek columns supporting front portico. Entry from side steps to double doors. Brick cupola rises from center of roof.

SV93-4

WOODBURY HOUSE

Turned spindle posts support front porch of clapboard home. Double gable design with lower gable featuring two story bow windows. Brick chimney extends through roof.

SV93-5

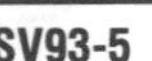

HUNTING LODGE

Rustic log structure on stone foundation and with stone fireplace. Antlers decorate front gable above porch entry.

SV93-6

DAIRY BARN

Cow barn with attached silo. Tin mansard roof. Cow weathervane.

SV93-7

DINAH'S DRIVE-IN

Burger in bun and bubbly soda top circular fast food drive-in.

SV93-8

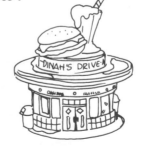

SNOWY HILLS HOSPITAL

Brick hospital, steps lead to double main doors with emergency entry drive-up on side.

ART CHART #	NAME	ITEM #	MATERIAL	SET?		MARKET STATUS	ORIGINAL SRP	GREENBOOK TRUMKT PRICE
	VARIATIONS/MISC/COLLECTOR NOTES							
SV93-1	NANTUCKET RENOVATION	5441-0	Ceramic	NO	✓	1993 ANNUAL	$ 55.00	$ 70.00
	Available only through retailers who carried Snow Village in 1986, Showcase Dealers, and select buying groups. For the original Nantucket see 1978, Item # 5014-6, (SV78-4), page 15. Special box and hang tag. Blueprints of renovation included.							
SV93-2	MOUNT OLIVET CHURCH	5442-9	Ceramic	NO	✓	CURRENT	65.00	65.00
SV93-3	VILLAGE PUBLIC LIBRARY	5443-7	Ceramic	NO	✓	CURRENT	55.00	55.00
SV93-4	WOODBURY HOUSE	5444-5	Ceramic	NO	✓	CURRENT	45.00	45.00
SV93-5	HUNTING LODGE	5445-3	Ceramic	NO	✓	CURRENT	50.00	50.00
SV93-6	DAIRY BARN	5446-1	Ceramic	NO	✓	CURRENT	55.00	55.00
SV93-7	DINAH'S DRIVE-IN	5447-0	Ceramic	NO	✓	CURRENT	45.00	45.00
SV93-8	SNOWY HILLS HOSPITAL	5448-8	Ceramic	NO	✓	CURRENT	48.00	48.00
	Portion of proceeds from sale of piece will be donated to AmFAR through the Gift For Life Foundation.							

SV94-1

FISHERMAN'S NOOK RESORT
Office/store for cabin rental, bait, and gas for boats, plus places for boats to tie up.

SV94-2

FISHERMAN'S NOOK CABINS:

FISHERMAN'S NOOK BASS CABIN
FISHERMAN'S NOOK TROUT CABIN

SV94-3

FISHERMAN'S NOOK BASS CABIN

SV94-4

FISHERMAN'S NOOK TROUT CABIN

Each cabin named for fish - rustic wood cabin with wood pile and fireplace for heat.

SV94-5

THE ORIGINAL SNOW VILLAGE STARTER SET
- Shady Oak Church
- Sunday School Serenade accessory
- three assorted "bottle-brush" sisal trees
- a bag of "Real Plastic Snow"

SHADY OAK CHURCH
Steeple rises above side entry to simple clapboard country church. Windows have pointed arch topped by trefoil design.

SUNDAY SCHOOL SERENADE
Choir boys sing carols.

ART CHART #	NAME	ITEM #	MATERIAL	SET?	!	MARKET STATUS	ORIGINAL SRP	GREENBOOK TRUMKT PRICE
	VARIATIONS/MISC/COLLECTOR NOTES							
SV94-1	FISHERMAN'S NOOK RESORT	5460-7	Ceramic	NO	✓	CURRENT	$ 75.00	$ 75.00
SV94-2	**FISHERMAN'S NOOK CABINS**	**5461-5**	**Ceramic**	**SET OF 2**	✓	**CURRENT**	**50.00**	**50.00**
	Midyear release.							
SV94-3	*FISHERMAN'S NOOK BASS CABIN*	5461-5	Ceramic	1 of a 2 pc set	✓	CURRENT	----	----
	Midyear release.							
SV94-4	*FISHERMAN'S NOOK TROUT CABIN*	5461-5	Ceramic	1 of a 2 pc set	✓	CURRENT	----	----
	Midyear release.							
SV94-5	THE ORIGINAL SNOW VILLAGE STARTER SET	5462-3	Ceramic	SET OF 6	✓	CURRENT	49.99	50.00
	Featured at D56 National Open Houses hosted by participating GCC retailers the first weekend in November 1994.							

. . . 1994 THE ORIGINAL SNOW VILLAGE . . . 1994

SV94-6

WEDDING CHAPEL

White clapboard church. Brick tower supports wooden steeple. Bell hangs in tower above door. Green shutters on arched windows.

SV94-7

FEDERAL HOUSE

Symmetrical brick structure has white portico and columns at front door. Dormers and four chimneys complete the mirrored effect.

SV94-8

CARMEL COTTAGE

Stucco walls, steep pitched roof, dormer on side and chimney at rear. Stone trims door, side passage and windows.

SV94-9

SKATE & SKI SHOP

Stone chimney and slate roof on chalet style shop. Timber trims windows and base.

SV94-10

GLENHAVEN HOUSE

2-1/2 story home with bay windows on first floor. Small porch at entrance. Two trees attached at right, front corner.

SV94-11

COCA-COLA BOTTLING PLANT

Large, red Coca-Cola logo sign set on roof above entry doors. Vending machine sits at back of loading dock, two cases sit at front. Two smoke stacks rise from roof near skylights.

SV94-12

MARVEL'S BEAUTY SALON

Brick 1st story houses Beauty Salon. Picture window displays styles. Stucco 2nd story houses Wig Shop.

ART CHART #	NAME	ITEM #	MATERIAL	SET?	!	MARKET STATUS	ORIGINAL SRP	GREENBOOK TRUMKT PRICE
	VARIATIONS/MISC/COLLECTOR NOTES							
SV94-6	WEDDING CHAPEL	5464-0	Ceramic	NO	✓	CURRENT	$ 55.00	$ 55.00
SV94-7	FEDERAL HOUSE	5465-8	Ceramic	NO	✓	CURRENT	50.00	50.00
	American Architecture Series.							
SV94-8	CARMEL COTTAGE	5466-6	Ceramic	NO	✓	CURRENT	48.00	48.00
SV94-9	SKATE & SKI SHOP	5467-4	Ceramic	NO	✓	CURRENT	50.00	50.00
SV94-10	GLENHAVEN HOUSE	5468-2	Ceramic	NO	✓	CURRENT	45.00	45.00
SV94-11	COCA-COLA BOTTLING PLANT	5469-0	Ceramic	NO	✓	CURRENT	65.00	65.00
	Prototypes did not have cases of soda on loading dock.							
SV94-12	MARVEL'S BEAUTY SALON	5470-4	Ceramic	NO	✓	CURRENT	37.50	37.50

SV95-1	SV95-2	SV95-3	
CHRISTMAS COVE LIGHTHOUSE Ship beacon atop white block tower. Steps lead to brick home of keeper. Attached trees.	**COCA-COLA CORNER DRUGSTORE** Oversize Coke bottle and logo sign is advertisement for soda shop in drugstore. Stone corner shop with bow windows and roof cornices.	**PEPPERMINT PORCH DAY CARE** Day care center in white clapboard house. Mint candy theme on pillars and balcony. Boots, teddy bear on porch.	

ART CHART #	NAME	ITEM #	MATERIAL	SET?	(lightbulb)	MARKET STATUS	ORIGINAL SRP	GREENBOOK TRUMKT PRICE
	VARIATIONS/MISC/COLLECTOR NOTES							
SV95-1	CHRISTMAS COVE LIGHTHOUSE	5483-6	Ceramic	NO	✓	CURRENT	$ 60.00	$ 60.00
	Midyear release. 2-light socket cord. Lift-off top allows access to bulb in tower.							
SV95-2	COCA-COLA CORNER DRUGSTORE	5484-4	Ceramic	NO	✓	CURRENT	55.00	55.00
	Midyear release.							
SV95-3	PEPPERMINT PORCH DAY CARE	5485-2	Ceramic	NO	✓	CURRENT	45.00	45.00
	Midyear release. Prototype had "Peppermint Place" as the name on the building.							

SVA79-1

CAROLERS
Couple, girl, garlanded lamppost, snowman.

SVA80-2

CERAMIC CAR
Open roadster holds lap rugs, Christmas tree, and wrapped presents.

SVA81-3

CERAMIC SLEIGH
Patterned after old fashioned wood sleigh, holds Christmas tree and wrapped presents.

SVA82-4

SNOWMAN WITH BROOM
Top hat, red nose, snowman holds straw broom.

SVA83-5

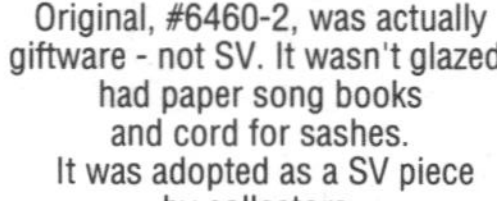
Original, #6460-2, was actually giftware - not SV. It wasn't glazed, had paper song books and cord for sashes. It was adopted as a SV piece by collectors.

MONKS-A-CAROLING
Four friars singing carols.

SVA84-6

SCOTTIE WITH TREE
Black dog waits by snow covered tree with star at top.

SVA84-7

MONKS-A-CAROLING
Four friars singing carols.

SVA85-8

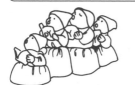

SINGING NUNS
Four nuns in habits, sing carols.

ART CHART #	NAME	ITEM #	MATERIAL	SET?	💡	MARKET STATUS	ORIGINAL SRP	GREENBOOK TRUMKT PRICE
	VARIATIONS/MISC/COLLECTOR NOTES							
SVA79-1	CAROLERS (1979)	5064-1	Ceramic	SET OF 4		RETIRED 1986	$ 12.00	$ 125.00
	First non-lit accessory.							
SVA80-2	CERAMIC CAR (1980)	5069-0	Ceramic	NO		RETIRED 1986	5.00	50.00
	First vehicle, no other cars available until 1985. Did not come in a box.							
SVA81-3	CERAMIC SLEIGH (1981)	5079-2	Ceramic	NO		RETIRED 1986	5.00	55.00
	Did not come in a box.							
SVA82-4	SNOWMAN WITH BROOM (1982)	5018-0	Ceramic*	NO		RETIRED 1990	3.00	10.00
	*Straw broom.							
SVA83-5	MONKS-A-CAROLING (1983)	6459-9	Ceramic	NO		RETIRED 1984	6.00	70.00
	Retired after just one year due to maker being unable to supply. On this piece, Monks have a diffused rosy blush. Re-introduced in 1984 as #5040-7 (SVA84-7) from another supplier. On later piece, Monks have a distinct pink circle to give cheeks blush.							
SVA84-6	SCOTTIE WITH TREE (1984)	5038-5	Ceramic	NO		RETIRED 1985	3.00	150.00
	Variation: with and without star at top of tree.							
SVA84-7	MONKS-A-CAROLING (1984)	5040-7	Ceramic	NO		RETIRED 1988	6.00	40.00
	Replaced 1983 Monks-A-Caroling #6459-9 (SVA83-5).							
SVA85-8	SINGING NUNS (1985)	5053-9	Ceramic	NO		RETIRED 1987	6.00	125.00

SVA85-9

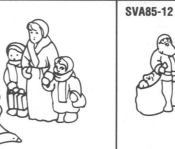

AUTO WITH TREE
Red VW Beetle with tree strapped to roof.

SVA85-10

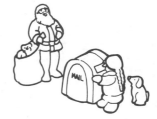

SNOW KIDS SLED, SKIS
Three children on a toboggan and one child on skis.

SVA85-11

FAMILY MOM/KIDS, GOOSE/GIRL
Mother holds hands of two children, one girl feeds corn to geese.

SVA85-12

SANTA/MAILBOX
Santa with toy bag. Girl mails letter to Santa as dog watches.

SVA86-13

KIDS AROUND THE TREE
Children join hands to make a ring around the snow covered tree with a gold star.

SVA86-14

GIRL/SNOWMAN, BOY
Girl puts finishing touches on snowman as boy reaches to place decorated hat atop head.

SVA86-15

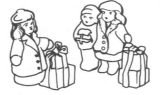

SHOPPING GIRLS WITH PACKAGES
Girls dressed toasty for shopping with hats, mittens, coats, boots, stand by some of their wrapped packages.

SVA87-16

WHITE PICKET FENCE
White metal decorative fence usually used at a private home or to define a formal garden.

ART CHART #	NAME	ITEM #	MATERIAL	SET?	!	MARKET STATUS	ORIGINAL SRP	GREENBOOK TRUMKT PRICE
	VARIATIONS/MISC/COLLECTOR NOTES							
SVA85-9	AUTO WITH TREE (1985)	5055-5	Ceramic/Sisal	NO		CURRENT	$ 5.00	$ 6.50
	Sisal tree attached. Did not come in box. 1st issue looks as if the tree's weight crushed the car. 1st approx. 3-3/8" long, 2nd approx. 3" long.							
SVA85-10	SNOW KIDS SLED, SKIS (1985)	5056-3	Ceramic	SET OF 2		RETIRED 1987	11.00	50.00
	See "Snow Kids," 1987, #5113-6 (SVA87-24).							
SVA85-11	FAMILY MOM/KIDS, GOOSE/GIRL (1985)	5057-1	Ceramic	SET OF 2		RETIRED 1988	11.00	45.00
	Variations in size.							
SVA85-12	SANTA/MAILBOX (1985)	5059-8	Ceramic	SET OF 2		RETIRED 1988	11.00	50.00
	Variations in size - larger Santa before downscaled was 3.2", new Santa with trimmer silhouette is 3".							
SVA86-13	KIDS AROUND THE TREE (1986)	5094-6	Ceramic	NO		RETIRED 1990	15.00	35.00
	Variations in size. Dramatically scaled down 5.75" to 4.5". GREENBOOK TRUMARKET Price for larger, pre-1987 piece, is $60.00.							
SVA86-14	GIRL/SNOWMAN, BOY (1986)	5095-4	Ceramic	SET OF 2		RETIRED 1987	11.00	70.00
	See "Snow Kids," 1987, #5113-6 (SVA87-24).							
SVA86-15	SHOPPING GIRLS WITH PACKAGES (1986)	5096-2	Ceramic	SET OF 2		RETIRED 1988	11.00	45.00
	Variations in size - 3" vs. 2.75", pre-1987 pieces are larger.							
SVA87-16	WHITE PICKET FENCE (1987)	5100-4	Metal	NO		CURRENT	3.00	3.00
	Size is 6" x 1.75". One of the first metal accessories (other was Park Bench). Also available in a set of 4, Item #5101-2, @ $12.00 SRP.							

SVA87-17

3 NUNS WITH SONGBOOKS
Three nuns in habits carry songbooks to sing carols.

SVA87-18

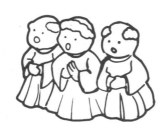

PRAYING MONKS
Three monks, standing side-by-side, praying.

SVA87-19

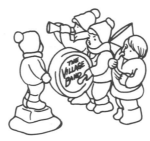

CHILDREN IN BAND
One child conducts three band players: horn, drum, and tuba.

SVA87-20

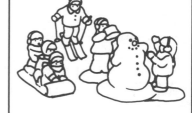

CAROLING FAMILY
Father holds baby, mother and son, and girl with pup.

SVA87-21

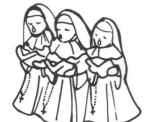

TAXI CAB
Yellow Checker cab.

SVA87-22

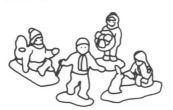

CHRISTMAS CHILDREN
Children at outdoor activities: girl and pup on sled pulled by boy, girl holding wreath, girl feeding carrot to bunny.

SVA87-23

FOR SALE SIGN
Holly decorates a house for sale sign. Usually sign post inserted at edge of property to be seen by people passing by.

SVA87-24

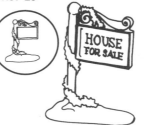

SNOW KIDS
Three kids on toboggan, child on skis, boy and girl putting finishing touches on snowman.

ART CHART #	NAME	ITEM #	MATERIAL	SET?		MARKET STATUS	ORIGINAL SRP	GREENBOOK TRUMKT PRICE
	VARIATIONS/MISC/COLLECTOR NOTES							
SVA87-17	3 NUNS WITH SONGBOOKS (1987)	5102-0	Ceramic	NO		RETIRED 1988	$ 6.00	$ 125.00
SVA87-18	PRAYING MONKS (1987)	5103-9	Ceramic	NO		RETIRED 1988	6.00	40.00
SVA87-19	CHILDREN IN BAND (1987)	5104-7	Ceramic	NO		RETIRED 1989	15.00	25.00
SVA87-20	CAROLING FAMILY (1987)	5105-5	Ceramic	SET OF 3		RETIRED 1990	20.00	30.00
SVA87-21	TAXI CAB (1987)	5106-3	Ceramic	NO		CURRENT	6.00	6.50
SVA87-22	CHRISTMAS CHILDREN (1987)	5107-1	Ceramic	SET OF 4		RETIRED 1990	20.00	30.00
SVA87-23	FOR SALE SIGN (1987)	5108-0	Ceramic	NO		RETIRED 1989	3.50	10.00
	Variation: blank sign for personalization, #581-9, Gift Creations Concepts 1989 Christmas Catalog Exclusive, free w/$100 Dept. 56 purchase.							
SVA87-24	SNOW KIDS (1987)	5113-6	Ceramic	SET OF 4		RETIRED 1990	20.00	45.00
	Set of 4 incorporates 1985 #5056-3 (SVA85-10) and 1986 #5095-4 (SVA86-14), re-scaled to the smaller size.							

SVA88-25

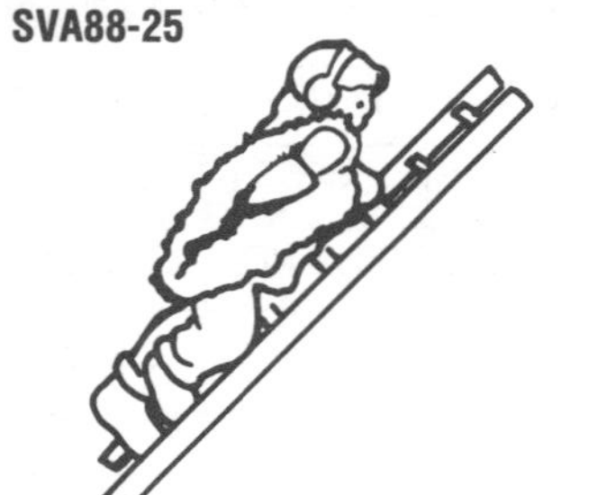

MAN ON LADDER HANGING GARLAND
Man carries garland up ladder to decorate eaves of house.

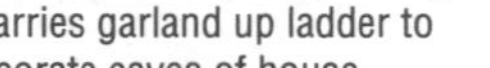

SVA88-26

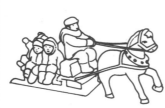

HAYRIDE
Farmer guides horse-drawn hay-filled sleigh with children as riders.

SVA88-27

SCHOOL CHILDREN
Three children carrying school books.

SVA88-28

APPLE GIRL/NEWSPAPER BOY
Girl holds wood tray carrier selling apples for 5¢, newsboy sells the Village News.

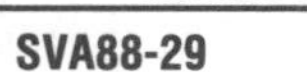

SVA88-29

WOODSMAN AND BOY
Man chops and splits logs and boy prepares to carry supply to fireplace.

SVA88-30

DOGHOUSE/CAT IN GARBAGE CAN
Dog sits outside doghouse decorated with wreath; cat looks at empty boxes and wrappings in garbage can.

SVA88-31

FIRE HYDRANT AND MAILBOX
Red fire hydrant and rural curbside mailbox on post.

SVA88-32

WATER TOWER
Metal scaffold base holds red ceramic water container with green top, ladder leads to top.

ART CHART #	NAME	ITEM #	MATERIAL	SET?	!	MARKET STATUS	ORIGINAL SRP	GREENBOOK TRUMKT PRICE
	VARIATIONS/MISC/COLLECTOR NOTES							
SVA88-25	MAN ON LADDER HANGING GARLAND (1988)	5116-0	See Below*	NO		RETIRED 1992	$ 7.50	$ 18.00
	*Ladder is wooden, garland is fiber, man is ceramic.							
SVA88-26	HAYRIDE (1988)	5117-9	Ceramic	NO		RETIRED 1990	30.00	60.00
SVA88-27	SCHOOL CHILDREN (1988)	5118-7	Ceramic	SET OF 3		RETIRED 1990	15.00	25.00
SVA88-28	APPLE GIRL/NEWSPAPER BOY (1988)	5129-2	Ceramic	SET OF 2		RETIRED 1990	11.00	20.00
SVA88-29	WOODSMAN AND BOY (1988)	5130-6	Ceramic	SET OF 2		RETIRED 1991	13.00	30.00
SVA88-30	DOGHOUSE/CAT IN GARBAGE CAN (1988)	5131-4	Ceramic	SET OF 2		RETIRED 1992	15.00	25.00
SVA88-31	FIRE HYDRANT AND MAILBOX (1988)	5132-2	Metal	SET OF 2		CURRENT	6.00	6.00
	Sizes are 1.5" and 2.75", respectively.							
SVA88-32	WATER TOWER (1988)	5133-0	Metal/Ceramic	2 PIECES		RETIRED 1991	20.00	65.00
	"John Deere Co." Water Tower (1989), #2510-4, Original SRP was $24.00 + Shipping. GREENBOOK TRUMARKET Price is $650.00.							

. . . Accessories . . . THE ORIGINAL SNOW VILLAGE . . . Accessories . . .

SVA88-33

NATIVITY

Holy Family, lamb, in creche scene.

SVA88-34

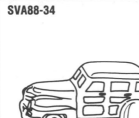

WOODY STATION WAGON

"Wood" paneled sides on station wagon.

SVA88-35

SCHOOL BUS, SNOW PLOW

Yellow school bus and red sand gravel truck with snow plow.

SVA88-36

TREE LOT

Christmas lights on tree lot's fence plus decorated shack and trees for sale.

SVA88-37

UP ON A ROOF TOP

Santa and sleigh pulled by eight reindeer.

SVA88-38

SISAL TREE LOT

A variety of cut trees for sale at a street lot.

SVA89-39

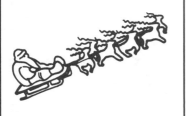

VILLAGE GAZEBO

Small, open, red roofed garden structure that will protect folks from rain/snow, or be a private place to sit.

SVA89-40

CHOIR KIDS

Four kids in white and red robes with green songbooks caroling.

ART CHART #	NAME	ITEM #	MATERIAL	SET?	💡	MARKET STATUS	ORIGINAL SRP	GREENBOOK TRUMKT PRICE
	VARIATIONS/MISC/COLLECTOR NOTES							
SVA88-33	NATIVITY (1988)	5135-7	Ceramic	NO		CURRENT	$ 7.50	$ 7.50
	Size is 2.25".							
SVA88-34	WOODY STATION WAGON (1988)	5136-5	Ceramic	NO		RETIRED 1990	6.50	25.00
SVA88-35	SCHOOL BUS, SNOW PLOW (1988)	5137-3	Ceramic	SET OF 2		RETIRED 1991	16.00	50.00
SVA88-36	TREE LOT (1988)	5138-1	See Below*	NO		CURRENT	33.50	37.50
	*Sisal trees, wood fence, ceramic shack.							
SVA88-37	UP ON A ROOF TOP (1988)	5139-0	Pewter	2 PIECES		CURRENT	6.50	6.50
	Size is 4" long.							
SVA88-38	SISAL TREE LOT (1988)	8183-3	Sisal	NO		RETIRED 1991	45.00	75.00
SVA89-39	VILLAGE GAZEBO (1989)	5146-2	Ceramic	NO		CURRENT	27.00	30.00
SVA89-40	CHOIR KIDS (1989)	5147-0	Ceramic	NO		RETIRED 1992	15.00	25.00

SVA89-41

SPECIAL DELIVERY
Mailman and mailbag with his mail truck in USPO colors red, white, and blue with the eagle logo.

SVA89-42

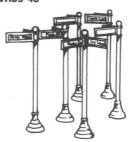

FOR SALE SIGN
Enameled metal sign can be "For Sale" or "SOLD." Birds decorate and add color.

SVA89-43

STREET SIGN
Green street signs can be personalized to give each village street a unique name.

SVA89-44

KIDS TREE HOUSE
Decorated club house built on an old dead tree. Steps lead up to hideaway.

SVA89-45

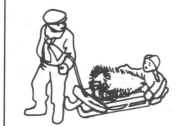

BRINGING HOME THE TREE
Man pulls sled holding tree as girl watches to make sure it doesn't fall off.

SVA89-46

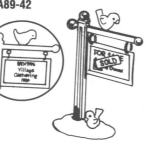

SKATE FASTER MOM
Two children sit in sleigh as skating Mom pushes them across the ice.

SVA89-47

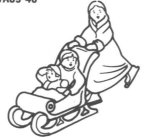

CRACK THE WHIP
Fast moving line of skaters hold tightly to person in front of them. First person does slow patterns but as line snakes out, last people are racing to keep up and they whip out.

SVA89-48

THROUGH THE WOODS
Children bring tree and basket of goodies to Grandma.

ART CHART #	NAME	ITEM #	MATERIAL	SET?	!	MARKET STATUS	ORIGINAL SRP	GREENBOOK TRUMKT PRICE
	VARIATIONS/MISC/COLLECTOR NOTES							
SVA89-41	SPECIAL DELIVERY (1989)	5148-9	Ceramic	SET OF 2		RETIRED 1990	$ 16.00	$ 45.00
	Discontinued due to licensing problems with the U.S. Postal Service. Replaced with 1990 Special Delivery #5197-7 (SVA90-66).							
SVA89-42	FOR SALE SIGN (1989)	5166-7	Metal	NO		CURRENT	4.50	4.50
	Size is 3" tall. Insert illustrates #539-8, Bachman's exclusive Village Gathering 1990 "For Sale" sign. GREENBOOK TRUMKT Price is $25.							
SVA89-43	STREET SIGN (1989)	5167-5	Metal	6 PCS/PKG		DISCONTINUED	7.50	8.00
	Use street names provided (Lake St., Maple Dr., Park Ave., River Rd., Elm St., Ivy Lane ...) or personalize. Size is 4.25" tall.							
SVA89-44	KIDS TREE HOUSE (1989)	5168-3	Resin	NO		RETIRED 1991	25.00	50.00
SVA89-45	BRINGING HOME THE TREE (1989)	5169-1	Ceramic/Sisal	NO		RETIRED 1992	15.00	25.00
SVA89-46	SKATE FASTER MOM (1989)	5170-5	Ceramic	NO		RETIRED 1991	13.00	20.00
SVA89-47	CRACK THE WHIP (1989)	5171-3	Ceramic	SET OF 3		CURRENT	25.00	25.00
SVA89-48	THROUGH THE WOODS (1989)	5172-1	Ceramic/Sisal	SET OF 2		RETIRED 1991	18.00	25.00

SVA89-49

STATUE OF MARK TWAIN
Tribute to author who wrote about lives of American folk.

SVA89-50

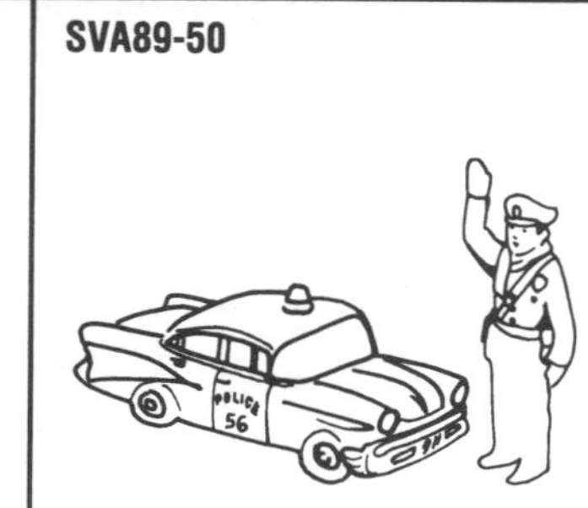

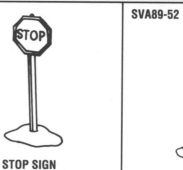

CALLING ALL CARS
Police car and patrolman directing traffic.

SVA89-51

STOP SIGN
Octagonal sign, placed on a corner or dangerous entry/exit to cause vehicles to come to a complete stop.

SVA89-52

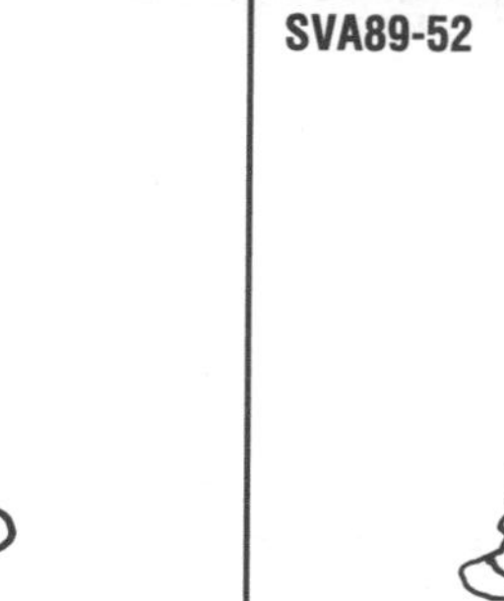

FLAG POLE
Pole with American flag to display in public.

SVA89-53

PARKING METER
You can still park for 5¢ in the Snow Village.

SVA89-54

MAILBOX
Freestanding public mailbox in USPO colors red, white, and blue with logo.

SVA89-55

VILLAGE WINTER BIRDS
Small red and blue sitting birds for use in decorating and as accessories.

SVA89-56

SNOW VILLAGE PROMOTIONAL SIGN
Displays Snow Village logo. Brickwork at base supports sign.

ART CHART #	NAME	ITEM #	MATERIAL	SET?	!	MARKET STATUS	ORIGINAL SRP	GREENBOOK TRUMKT PRICE
	VARIATIONS/MISC/COLLECTOR NOTES							
SVA89-49	STATUE OF MARK TWAIN (1989)	5173-0	Ceramic	NO		RETIRED 1991	$ 15.00	$ 30.00
SVA89-50	CALLING ALL CARS (1989)	5174-8	Ceramic	SET OF 2		RETIRED 1991	15.00	35.00
SVA89-51	STOP SIGN (1989)	5176-4	Metal	2 PCS/PKG		CURRENT	5.00	5.00
	Size is 3" tall.							
SVA89-52	FLAG POLE (1989)	5177-2	See Below*	NO		CURRENT	8.50	8.50
	*Resin base, metal pole, cloth flag, thread rope. Size is 7" tall.							
SVA89-53	PARKING METER (1989)	5178-0	Metal	4 PCS/PKG		CURRENT	6.00	6.00
	Size is 2" tall.							
SVA89-54	MAILBOX (1989)	5179-9	Metal	NO		RETIRED 1990	3.50	20.00
	Red, white & blue version. Discontinued due to licensing problems w/the USPO. Replaced with 1990 Mailbox #5198-5 (SVA90-67).							
SVA89-55	VILLAGE WINTER BIRDS (1989)	5180-2	Metal	6 PCS/PKG		RETIRED 1994	3.50	4.00
SVA89-56	SNOW VILLAGE PROMOTIONAL SIGN (1989)	9948-1	Earthenware	NO		DISC. 1990	Promo	15.00
	Intended to be used by Dept. 56 retailers as a promotional item.							

SVA90-57

KIDS DECORATING THE VILLAGE SIGN
Two children place garland on Snow Village Sign.

SVA90-58

DOWN THE CHIMNEY HE GOES
Santa with bag of toys enters chimney to make delivery on Christmas Eve.

SVA90-59

SNO-JET SNOWMOBILE
Snowmobile, red with silver trim, front ski runners and rear caterpillar treads.

SVA90-60

SLEIGHRIDE
Family rides in open old fashioned green sleigh pulled by one horse.

SVA90-61

HERE WE COME A CAROLING
Children and pet dog sing carols.

SVA90-62

HOME DELIVERY
Milkman and milk truck.

SVA90-63

FRESH FROZEN FISH
Ice Fisherman, Ice House.

SVA90-64

A TREE FOR ME
Snowman with top hat, corn cob pipe, and red muffler carries his own small snow covered tree.

ART CHART #	NAME	ITEM #	MATERIAL	SET?	💡	MARKET STATUS	ORIGINAL SRP	GREENBOOK TRUMKT PRICE
	VARIATIONS/MISC/COLLECTOR NOTES							
SVA90-57	KIDS DECORATING THE VILLAGE SIGN (1990)	5134-9	Ceramic	NO		RETIRED 1993	$ 12.50	$ 20.00
SVA90-58	DOWN THE CHIMNEY HE GOES (1990)	5158-6	Ceramic	NO		RETIRED 1993	6.50	14.00
SVA90-59	SNO-JET SNOWMOBILE (1990)	5159-4	Ceramic	NO		RETIRED 1993	15.00	24.00
SVA90-60	SLEIGHRIDE (1990)	5160-8	Ceramic	NO		RETIRED 1992	30.00	55.00
SVA90-61	HERE WE COME A CAROLING (1990)	5161-6	Ceramic	SET OF 3		RETIRED 1992	18.00	25.00
SVA90-62	HOME DELIVERY (1990)	5162-4	Ceramic	SET OF 2		RETIRED 1992	16.00	30.00
SVA90-63	FRESH FROZEN FISH (1990)	5163-2	Ceramic	SET OF 2		RETIRED 1993	20.00	35.00
SVA90-64	A TREE FOR ME (1990)	5164-0	Ceramic/Sisal	2 PCS/PKG		CURRENT	7.50	8.00

SVA90-65

A HOME FOR THE HOLIDAYS

Red and yellow birdhouse with blue bird sitting on roof. Pole decorated with garland and small snow covered evergreen.

SVA90-66

SPECIAL DELIVERY

Snow Village postman and truck in red & green Snow Village Mail Service colors.

SVA90-67

VILLAGE MAILBOX

Snow Village mail receptacle in red and green Snow Village Mail Service colors.

SVA90-68

CHRISTMAS TRASH CANS

Two galvanized refuse cans filled with holiday wrappings and garbage.

SVA91-69

WREATHS FOR SALE

Girl holds for sale sign, boy holds up wreaths, child pulls sled. Fence holds wreaths.

SVA91-70

WINTER FOUNTAIN

Angel holds sea shell with water frozen as it flowed.

SVA91-71

COLD WEATHER SPORTS

Three children play ice hockey.

SVA91-72

COME JOIN THE PARADE

Two children carry parade banner.

ART CHART #	NAME / VARIATIONS/MISC/COLLECTOR NOTES	ITEM #	MATERIAL	SET?	!	MARKET STATUS	ORIGINAL SRP	GREENBOOK TRUMKT PRICE
SVA90-65	A HOME FOR THE HOLIDAYS (1990)	5165-9	Ceramic	NO		CURRENT	$ 6.50	$ 7.00
SVA90-66	SPECIAL DELIVERY (1990)	5197-7	Ceramic	SET OF 2		RETIRED 1992	16.00	35.00
	"S.V. Mail" Service. Replaces discontinued 1985 Special Delivery #5148-9 (SVA89-41).							
SVA90-67	VILLAGE MAILBOX (1990)	5198-5	Metal	NO		CURRENT	3.50	3.50
	Size is 2". "S.V. Mail" Service. Replaces discontinued 1985 Mailbox #5179-9 (SVA89-54).							
SVA90-68	CHRISTMAS TRASH CANS (1990)	5209-4	See Below*	SET OF 2		CURRENT	6.50	7.00
	Size is 1.5". *Metal/Plastic/Paper. Tops come off.							
SVA91-69	WREATHS FOR SALE (1991)	5408-9	See Below*	SET OF 4		RETIRED 1994	27.50	45.00
	*Ceramic/Wood/Sisal.							
SVA91-70	WINTER FOUNTAIN (1991)	5409-7	See Below*	NO		RETIRED 1993	25.00	50.00
	*Ceramic/Acrylic.							
SVA91-71	COLD WEATHER SPORTS (1991)	5410-0	Ceramic	SET OF 4		RETIRED 1994	27.50	45.00
SVA91-72	COME JOIN THE PARADE (1991)	5411-9	Ceramic	NO		RETIRED 1992	12.50	20.00

SVA91-73

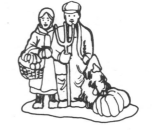

VILLAGE MARCHING BAND
Drum Major, two horn players, and two drummers.

SVA91-74

CHRISTMAS CADILLAC
Pink car holds tree and presents.

SVA91-75

SNOWBALL FORT
One boy behind wall, one hides behind tree, one in open clearing all with snowballs to throw.

SVA91-76

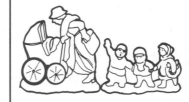

COUNTRY HARVEST
Farm folk with market basket and pitchfork. (Reminiscent of American Gothic painting.)

SVA91-77

VILLAGE GREETINGS
Holiday banners to hang on side of buildings.

SVA92-78

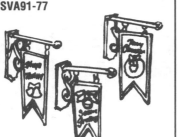

VILLAGE USED CAR LOT
Small wooden office on a stone base with stone chimney. Attached tree. Free standing sign plus office sign advertises used cars and good terms. Three cars in lot.

SVA92-79

VILLAGE PHONE BOOTH
Silver and red outdoor phone booth with accordion open/close doors.

SVA92-80

NANNY AND THE PRESCHOOLERS
Two girls and boy hold onto Nanny's shopping basket as she pushes carriage with baby.

ART CHART #	NAME	ITEM #	MATERIAL	SET?	!	MARKET STATUS	ORIGINAL SRP	GREENBOOK TRUMKT PRICE
	VARIATIONS/MISC/COLLECTOR NOTES							
SVA91-73	VILLAGE MARCHING BAND (1991)	5412-7	Ceramic	SET OF 3		RETIRED 1992	$ 30.00	$ 50.00
SVA91-74	CHRISTMAS CADILLAC (1991)	5413-5	Ceramic/Sisal	NO		RETIRED 1994	9.00	10.00
SVA91-75	SNOWBALL FORT (1991)	5414-3	Ceramic	SET OF 3		RETIRED 1993	27.50	40.00
SVA91-76	COUNTRY HARVEST (1991)	5415-1	Ceramic	NO		RETIRED 1993	13.00	25.00
SVA91-77	VILLAGE GREETINGS (1991)	5418-6	Metal	SET OF 3		RETIRED 1994	5.00	10.00
SVA92-78	VILLAGE USED CAR LOT (1992)	5428-3	Ceramic	SET OF 5		CURRENT	45.00	45.00
SVA92-79	VILLAGE PHONE BOOTH (1992)	5429-1	Ceramic	NO		CURRENT	7.50	7.50
SVA92-80	NANNY AND THE PRESCHOOLERS (1992)	5430-5	Ceramic	SET OF 2		RETIRED 1994	27.50	30.00

SVA92-81

EARLY MORNING DELIVERY

Village kids deliver morning newspaper. One tosses to house, one pushes sled, and Dalmatian holds next paper in mouth.

SVA92-82

CHRISTMAS PUPPIES

One girl hugs a pup as two kids take box of pups for a ride in red wagon.

SVA92-83

ROUND & ROUND WE GO!

Two kids go sledding on round saucer sleds.

SVA92-84

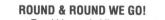

A HEAVY SNOWFALL

Girl stops to look at bird perched on handle of her shovel as boy shovels snow off the walkway.

SVA92-85

WE'RE GOING TO A CHRISTMAS PAGEANT

Children wear costumes of Santa, a decorated tree and a golden star.

SVA92-86

WINTER PLAYGROUND

Two swings and a playground slide. Two trees and two birds complete piece.

SVA92-87

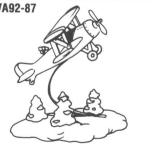

SPIRIT OF SNOW VILLAGE AIRPLANE

Red prop biplane. Metal strap spring on three tree base allows positioning.

SVA93-88

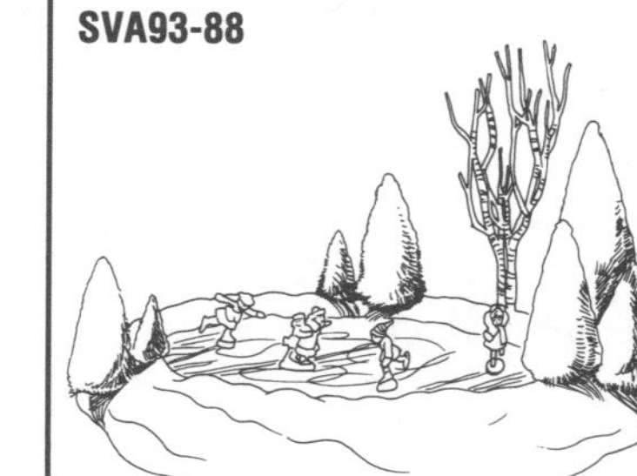

VILLAGE ANIMATED SKATING POND

Skaters move alone or as pair in set patterns on ice pond surface.

ART CHART #	NAME	ITEM #	MATERIAL	SET?	💡	MARKET STATUS	ORIGINAL SRP	GREENBOOK TRUMKT PRICE
	VARIATIONS/MISC/COLLECTOR NOTES							
SVA92-81	EARLY MORNING DELIVERY (1992)	5431-3	Ceramic	SET OF 3		CURRENT	$ 27.50	$ 27.50
SVA92-82	CHRISTMAS PUPPIES (1992)	5432-1	Ceramic	SET OF 2		CURRENT	27.50	27.50
SVA92-83	ROUND & ROUND WE GO! (1992)	5433-0	Ceramic	SET OF 2		CURRENT	18.00	18.00
SVA92-84	A HEAVY SNOWFALL (1992)	5434-8	Ceramic	SET OF 2		CURRENT	16.00	16.00
SVA92-85	WE'RE GOING TO A CHRISTMAS PAGEANT (1992)	5435-6	Ceramic	NO		RETIRED 1994	15.00	18.00
SVA92-86	WINTER PLAYGROUND (1992)	5436-4	Ceramic	NO		CURRENT	20.00	20.00
SVA92-87	SPIRIT OF SNOW VILLAGE AIRPLANE (1992)	5440-2	Ceramic/Metal	NO		CURRENT	32.50	32.50
SVA93-88	VILLAGE ANIMATED SKATING POND (1993)	5229-9	-------	SET OF 15		CURRENT	60.00	60.00
	Electrical.							

SVA93-89

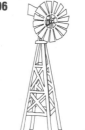

SAFETY PATROL

Older children are safety guards at street crossing for 2 younger children.

SVA93-90

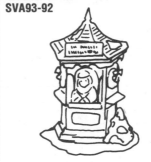

CHRISTMAS AT THE FARM

Calf and lamb greet girl carrying a pail of feed.

SVA93-91

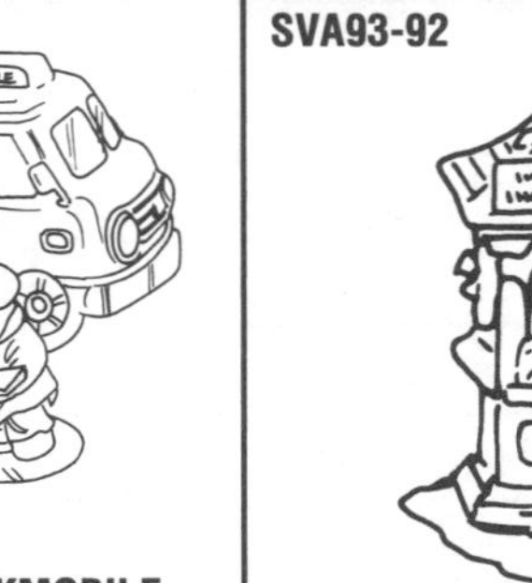

CHECK IT OUT BOOKMOBILE

Bookmobile van carries stories to children in villages and farms. Boys and girls select books to borrow.

SVA93-92

TOUR THE VILLAGE

Tourist information booth with clerk to assist visitors new to the village.

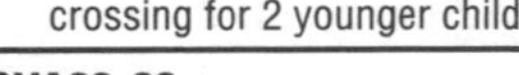

SVA93-93

PINT-SIZE PONY RIDES

One child waits to buy a pony ride as another rides and one offers carrot to pony. Stable building and bench for man with pony ride and 3 children.

SVA93-94

PICK-UP AND DELIVERY

Pickup truck carries Christmas tree.

SVA93-95

A HERD OF HOLIDAY HEIFERS

3 Holstein cows.

SVA93-96

WINDMILL

Metal base holds blades that turn in wind to produce electricity.

ART CHART #	NAME	ITEM #	MATERIAL	SET?	!	MARKET STATUS	ORIGINAL SRP	GREENBOOK TRUMKT PRICE
	VARIATIONS/MISC/COLLECTOR NOTES							
SVA93-89	SAFETY PATROL (1993)	5449-6	Ceramic	SET OF 4		CURRENT	$ 27.50	$ 27.50
SVA93-90	CHRISTMAS AT THE FARM (1993)	5450-0	Ceramic	SET OF 2		CURRENT	16.00	16.00
SVA93-91	CHECK IT OUT BOOKMOBILE (1993)	5451-8	Ceramic	SET OF 3		CURRENT	25.00	25.00
SVA93-92	TOUR THE VILLAGE (1993)	5452-6	Ceramic	NO		CURRENT	12.50	12.50
	Bayport is misspelled. Has "q" instead of "p."							
SVA93-93	PINT-SIZE PONY RIDES (1993)	5453-4	Ceramic	SET OF 3		CURRENT	37.50	37.50
SVA93-94	PICK-UP AND DELIVERY (1993)	5454-2	Ceramic	NO		CURRENT	10.00	10.00
SVA93-95	A HERD OF HOLIDAY HEIFERS (1993)	5455-0	Ceramic	SET OF 3		CURRENT	18.00	18.00
SVA93-96	WINDMILL (1993)	5456-9	Metal/Earthen	NO		CURRENT	20.00	20.00
	Size is 11.5".							

SVA93-97

CLASSIC CARS
Station wagon with roof rack.
Two tone green sedan with tail fins.
Sedan with spare tire
mounted outside trunk.

SVA93-98

SPIRIT OF SNOW VILLAGE AIRPLANE
Propeller double strut winged planes.

SVA93-99

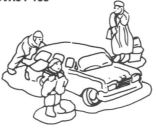

VILLAGE NEWS DELIVERY
Driver carries newspaper from van to stores and home delivery children carriers.

SVA94-100

VILLAGE STREETCAR
Track setup for inner city traveling.
Car lights up.
Passengers visible through windows.

SVA94-101

CAROLING AT THE FARM
Farmer drives tractor/pulls carolers on hay covered wagon. Child pulls another onto wagon.

SVA94-102

ALL AROUND THE PARK
People stroll through park on path that circles tree. Stone wall edges park and archway marks entrance.

SVA94-103

STUCK IN THE SNOW
Dad pushes car, mom watches and son holds shovel and sand.

SVA94-104

PETS ON PARADE
Two children walk dogs
on cold wintry day.

ART CHART #	NAME	ITEM #	MATERIAL	SET?	!	MARKET STATUS	ORIGINAL SRP	GREENBOOK TRUMKT PRICE
	VARIATIONS/MISC/COLLECTOR NOTES							
SVA93-97	CLASSIC CARS (1993)	5457-7	Ceramic	SET OF 3		CURRENT	$ 22.50	$ 22.50
SVA93-98	SPIRIT OF SNOW VILLAGE AIRPLANE (1993)	5458-5	Ceramic	2 ASST.*		CURRENT	12.50	12.50
	*2 Assorted; Blue, Yellow.							
SVA93-99	VILLAGE NEWS DELIVERY (1993)	5459-3	Ceramic	SET OF 2		CURRENT	15.00	15.00
SVA94-100	VILLAGE STREETCAR (1994)	5240-0	-------	SET OF 10		CURRENT	65.00	65.00
	Midyear release. Passenger's silhouettes on windows.							
SVA94-101	CAROLING AT THE FARM (1994)	5463-1	Ceramic	NO		CURRENT	35.00	35.00
	Midyear release. First ceramic accessory to be a midyear release.							
SVA94-102	ALL AROUND THE PARK (1994)	5247-7	-------	SET OF 18		CURRENT	95.00	95.00
SVA94-103	STUCK IN THE SNOW (1994)	5471-2	Ceramic	SET OF 3		CURRENT	30.00	30.00
SVA94-104	PETS ON PARADE (1994)	5472-0	Ceramic	SET OF 2		CURRENT	16.50	16.50

SVA94-105

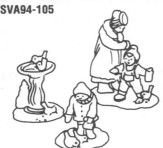

FEEDING THE BIRDS
Woman and children are feeding birds as other birds sit on frozen birdbath.

SVA94-106

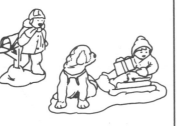

MUSH!
Small child sits on sled that is harnessed to a St. Bernard. Older child shouts to them from behind mailbox.

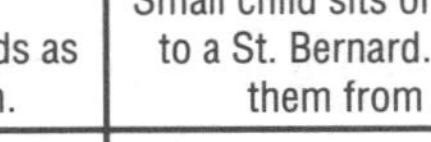

SVA94-107

SKATERS & SKIERS
One child laces up her skates while another is happy to be able to stand. As one skier looks on, another goes boom.

SVA94-108

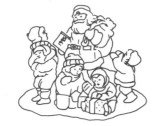

GOING TO THE CHAPEL
Family walks to the chapel with gifts and wreath as clergyman waits to greet them.

SVA94-109

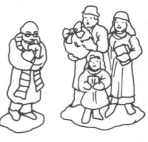

SANTA COMES TO TOWN
Children circle Santa as he passes out presents. He is holding a sack of toys and a book dated 1995.

SVA94-110

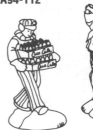

MARSHMALLOW ROAST
Children take skating rest and roast marshmallows over log fire.

SVA94-111

COCA-COLA DELIVERY TRUCK
A large wreath encircles "Coca-Cola" on the back of a red & white delivery truck.

SVA94-112

COCA-COLA DELIVERY MEN
One man carries crates to truck as another stops to taste a Coke.

ART CHART #	NAME	ITEM #	MATERIAL	SET?	!	MARKET STATUS	ORIGINAL SRP	GREENBOOK TRUMKT PRICE
	VARIATIONS/MISC/COLLECTOR NOTES							
SVA94-105	FEEDING THE BIRDS (1994)	5473-9	Ceramic	SET OF 3		CURRENT	$ 25.00	$ 25.00
SVA94-106	MUSH! (1994)	5474-7	Ceramic	SET OF 2		CURRENT	20.00	20.00
SVA94-107	SKATERS & SKIERS (1994)	5475-5	Ceramic	SET OF 3		CURRENT	27.50	27.50
SVA94-108	GOING TO THE CHAPEL (1994)	5476-3	Ceramic	SET OF 3		CURRENT	20.00	20.00
SVA94-109	SANTA COMES TO TOWN, 1995 (1994)	5477-1	Ceramic	NO		1995 ANNUAL	30.00	30.00
	Ist in a series of dated annual "Santa" pieces.							
SVA94-110	MARSHMALLOW ROAST (1994)	5478-0	Ceramic	SET OF 3	✓	CURRENT	32.50	32.50
	Battery operated fire glows.							
SVA94-111	COCA-COLA DELIVERY TRUCK (1994)	5479-8	Ceramic	NO		CURRENT	15.00	15.00
SVA94-112	COCA-COLA DELIVERY MEN (1994)	5480-1	Ceramic	SET OF 2		CURRENT	25.00	25.00

SVA94-113

COCA-COLA BILLBOARD

Three lights shine on billboard featuring Santa enjoying a Coke. Trees grow in the shade of the sign.

ART CHART #	NAME	ITEM #	MATERIAL	SET?	(lightbulb icon)	MARKET STATUS	ORIGINAL SRP	GREENBOOK TRUMKT PRICE
	VARIATIONS/MISC/COLLECTOR NOTES							
SVA95-113	COCA-COLA BILLBOARD (1994)	5481-0	Ceramic	NO		CURRENT	$ 18.00	$ 18.00

MDW79-1

THATCHED COTTAGE
Small thatched cottage with attached tree. Chimney at rear of stucco and timber trim.

MDW79-2

COUNTRYSIDE CHURCH
Countryside Church in a springtime setting. Large green tree against a simple white wood church with steeple rising from entry to nave.

MDW79-3

ASPEN TREES
The trees that shiver and tremble in the wind. Small leaves on a hardwood tree.

MDW79-4

SHEEP
Grazing white and black sheep make up this flock.

MEADOWLAND (COMPOSITE)

ART CHART #	NAME	ITEM #	MATERIAL	SET?	!	MARKET STATUS	ORIGINAL SRP	GREENBOOK TRUMKT PRICE
	VARIATIONS/MISC/COLLECTOR NOTES							
MDW79-1	THATCHED COTTAGE	5050-0	Ceramic	NO	✓	RETIRED 1980	$ 30.00	$ 795.00
MDW79-2	COUNTRYSIDE CHURCH	5051-8	Ceramic	NO	✓	RETIRED 1980	25.00	795.00
	For snow version see 1979 Countryside Church #5058-3 (SV79-5).							
MDW79-3	ASPEN TREES (ACCESSORY)	5052-6	Ceramic	NO		RETIRED 1980	16.00	NE
MDW79-4	SHEEP (ACCESSORY)	5053-4	Ceramic	SET OF 12		RETIRED 1980	12.00	NE
	9 white, 3 black.							

CLIPBOARD
- Technically not part of the Original Snow Village. Limited distribution.

NE = Not Established

BHS87-1

HOMETOWN BOARDING HOUSE

Three story brick building with rented rooms above main floor parlor and dining room. Ground floor has front bay window adjacent to covered entry porch which extends around side to windowed area. Second story features arched windows. Brick turret-like structures appear attached to rectangular design. Taller turret has windows on all four sides of roof with attic used for rental or storage.

BHS87-2

HOMETOWN CHURCH

Cross-shaped floor plan with spire rising from one side of transept. Simple entry door at base of spire in contrast to large arched windows that fill end walls.

BHS88-1

HOMETOWN DRUGSTORE

Drugstore is corner store in a two attached buildings structure. Taller three story building houses barber shop on main level and eye glass shop above. Entry to drugstore is at corner of shorter building with three support columns providing an open area to entry and for support of upper windowed turret design. Garlands decorate the awnings over display windows.

ART CHART #	NAME	ITEM #	MATERIAL	SET?	(lightbulb)	MARKET STATUS	ORIGINAL SRP	GREENBOOK TRUMKT PRICE
	VARIATIONS/MISC/COLLECTOR NOTES							
BHS87-1	HOMETOWN BOARDING HOUSE	670-0	Porcelain	NO	✓	RETIRED 1988	$ 34.00	$ 325.00
	Inspired by Sprague House in Red Wing, MN.							
BHS87-2	HOMETOWN CHURCH	671-8	Porcelain	NO	✓	RETIRED 1988	40.00	325.00
	Designed after a St. Paul, MN church.							
BHS88-1	HOMETOWN DRUGSTORE	672-6	Porcelain	NO	✓	RETIRED 1989	40.00	625.00
	Same mold as the Christmas In The City Variety Store, #5972-2, (CIC88-4). Inspired by a store in Stillwater, MN.							

CLIPBOARD

- Pieces were available in stores as a "Purchase With Purchase."
- Fourth piece, a Bookstore, was created to fit snugly against the Drugstore but was never produced.

continued from page 9

During the past couple of years I've noticed something that has caused me to stop and think. Many collectors refer to Mr. Ed Bazinet, the creator, CEO and Chairman of Department 56, as Ed. Although few collectors have had the pleasure of meeting this gentleman, they feel comfortable enough to mention him by his first name. This is just one example of how many friends we make collecting these little villages - some we haven't even met, yet.

Q. *What is the date on the bottom of the piece?*

Q. *I become very confused between when new pieces are actually available for purchase vs. the "Year Issued" indicated on D56's Item History List.*

A. The date on the bottom of the piece indicates the year in which the item was copyrighted by Department 56.

The Copyright protects the item from unauthorized duplication. The insignia is a circled "C" followed by the Department 56 Logotype and then the date. The copyright date is generally, but not always, the year before a piece is available in stores.

On the other hand, the May Midyear Introductions are generally copyrighted, introduced and available at your retailer in the same calendar year. Prior to 1994, pieces announced at midyear were usually only available to select groups of retailers as "early releases" that same year. Other authorized dealers had to wait until the following January.

"Year Issued" is synonymous with Copyright Date on the D56 Item History Lists.

Q. *I have heard pieces referred to as "exclusives," yet these particular pieces are available at all stores selling that particular line. Is this a misnomer?*

A. Actually, the term is a little confusing. Often, Department 56 allows a specific group of retailers the right to offer a particular piece to their collectors in advance of all other retailers. Traditionally, this has been a way for companies to reward very supportive dealers. These groups include "Key" Dealers, Showcase Dealers and Retail buying groups. Though collectors often refer to these as *exclusives*, they are really *early releases*. Usually they are available to the select groups during the Fall and are only "exclusive" until general release to all authorized retailers the following January.

Q. *Please explain the terms "Swap & Sell" and "Room Hopping."*

A. A Swap & Sell is an event where collectors and dealers meet to buy, sell and swap collectibles. The items being traded are usually no longer available at retail, sometimes called the primary market. I say usually because currently available product does show up from time to time. A Swap & Sell can be the main event, or part of a larger event like a Convention or Village Gathering.

Most often the Swap & Sell is sponsored by an organizer who rents the hall, advertises and provides a congenial atmosphere for all attendees. Collectors and Secondary Market dealers rent tables and display their wares. Swap & Sells are wonderful for purchasing secondary pieces because you often have a large selection.

A Room Hop is usually part of a bigger event. Collectors who stay at the same hotel while attending an event often participate in a Room Hop. On the designated evening those with items to trade will leave their doors open for a predetermined time. Collectors roam the halls, visiting open-door rooms, buying retired pieces and making new friends. They are always lots of fun.

continued on page 140

DV84-1

THE ORIGINAL SHOPS OF DICKENS' VILLAGE:

CROWNTREE INN
CANDLE SHOP
GREEN GROCER
GOLDEN SWAN BAKER
BEAN AND SON SMITHY SHOP
ABEL BEESLEY BUTCHER
JONES & CO.
BRUSH & BASKET SHOP

DV84-2

CROWNTREE INN

Large multi-paned windows run length of front of Inn with entry door decorated by wreath, second story stone, attic dormer.

DV84-3

CANDLE SHOP

Timber framed windows, plaster over stone small house/store. Rental rooms in attic, light over open front door.

DV84-4

GREEN GROCER

Thatched roof over timbered two story grocery/provisions store. Bay window for display. Attached storage room on side of store.

DV84-5

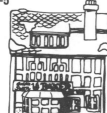

GOLDEN SWAN BAKER

Painted sign with gold swan hangs above large bay window for display. Timbered building, brick chimney, light above entry door.

DV84-6

BEAN AND SON SMITHY SHOP

Double wood door, stone first story, second story set on stone with overhang. Steep curved roof with brick chimney.

DV84-7

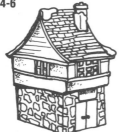

ABEL BEESLEY BUTCHER

Timbered bottom half, second story plaster over stone, two chimneys.

DV84-8

JONES & CO. BRUSH & BASKET SHOP

Cellar shop is a cobbler with small sign by his door to advertise, rest of building is for basketry, mats, and brush. Narrow staircase leads to entry.

ART CHART #	NAME	ITEM #	MATERIAL	SET?	!	MARKET STATUS	ORIGINAL SRP	GREENBOOK TRUMKT PRICE
	VARIATIONS/MISC/COLLECTOR NOTES							
DV84-1	**THE ORIGINAL SHOPS OF DICKENS' VILLAGE**	**6515-3**	**Porcelain**	**SET OF 7**	✓	**RETIRED 1988**	**$ 175.00**	**$ 1295.00**
DV84-2	*CROWNTREE INN*	6515-3	Porcelain	1 of a 7 pc set	✓	RETIRED 1988	25.00	300.00
DV84-3	*CANDLE SHOP*	6515-3	Porcelain	1 of a 7 pc set	✓	RETIRED 1988	25.00	190.00
	Variations in roof color - gray was first release, blue was subsequent.							
DV84-4	*GREEN GROCER*	6515-3	Porcelain	1 of a 7 pc set	✓	RETIRED 1988	25.00	185.00
DV84-5	*GOLDEN SWAN BAKER*	6515-3	Porcelain	1 of a 7 pc set	✓	RETIRED 1988	25.00	180.00
DV84-6	*BEAN AND SON SMITHY SHOP*	6515-3	Porcelain	1 of a 7 pc set	✓	RETIRED 1988	25.00	195.00
DV84-7	*ABEL BEESLEY BUTCHER*	6515-3	Porcelain	1 of a 7 pc set	✓	RETIRED 1988	25.00	125.00
DV84-8	*JONES & CO. BRUSH & BASKET SHOP*	6515-3	Porcelain	1 of a 7 pc set	✓	RETIRED 1988	25.00	300.00

1985 THE HERITAGE VILLAGE COLLECTION – DICKENS' VILLAGE 1985

DV85-1

DICKENS' VILLAGE CHURCH

Stone church with entry at base of massive turret. Nave has exposed stone base with timber/plaster upper walls. Irregular shingled roof. Entry door and nave windows have a pointed arch shape.

DV85-2

DICKENS' COTTAGES:

THATCHED COTTAGE
STONE COTTAGE
TUDOR COTTAGE

DV85-3

THATCHED COTTAGE

Double chimneys rise from thatched roof, second story plastered/timbered home with second story extending out on sides.

DV85-4

STONE COTTAGE

Varigated fieldstone walls crowned with rough-hewn shingle roof. House has two wings each with own chimney.

DV85-5

TUDOR COTTAGE

Stone foundation with timbered/plastered walls forming a small house. Two chimneys for heating/cooking.

DV85-6

DICKENS' VILLAGE MILL

Rough-hewn stone makes up 3 section mill with large wooden millwheel. Two sets double doors – one large set to allow carriage to be brought directly into building, smaller doors open into silo area. Pronounced roof ridges on two sections.

ART CHART #	NAME	ITEM #	MATERIAL	SET?	💡	MARKET STATUS	ORIGINAL SRP	GREENBOOK TRUMKT PRICE
	VARIATIONS/MISC/COLLECTOR NOTES							
DV85-1	DICKENS' VILLAGE CHURCH	6516-1	Porcelain	NO	✓	RETIRED 1989	$ 35.00	See Below*
	Variations in color affect TRUMARKET Price; see footnote[1] below.							
DV85-2	**DICKENS' COTTAGES**	**6518-8**	**Porcelain**	**SET OF 3**	✓	**RETIRED 1988**	**75.00**	**950.00**
	Early release to Gift Creations Concepts.							
DV85-3	*THATCHED COTTAGE*	6518-8	Porcelain	1 of a 3 pc set	✓	RETIRED 1988	25.00	200.00
	Early release to Gift Creations Concepts.							
DV85-4	*STONE COTTAGE*	6518-8	Porcelain	1 of a 3 pc set	✓	RETIRED 1988	25.00	400.00
	Early release to Gift Creations Concepts. Variations in color: "early tan" and "pea green."							
DV85-5	*TUDOR COTTAGE*	6518-8	Porcelain	1 of a 3 pc set	✓	RETIRED 1988	25.00	400.00
	Early release to Gift Creations Concepts.							
DV85-6	DICKENS' VILLAGE MILL	6519-6	Porcelain	NO	✓	LTD. ED. 2,500	35.00	5000.00
	Early release to Gift Creations Concepts. Some sleeves read "Dickens' Village Cottage."							

*There are five variations of the **Village Church**:

a) *Winter White*: off white to cream walls, brown roof matches brown cornerstones - $375.00.
b) *Yellow or Cream*: cream walls with light yellow coloring in mortar between stones, butterscotch roof - $225.00.
c) *Green*: very light green tone on walls, butterscotch roof - $330.00.
d) *Tan*: tan walls, butterscotch roof - $190.00.
e) *"Dark" or Butterscotch*: walls are same color or nearly the same as roof - $155.00.
(Only sleeve to read "Village Church." All others read "Shops Of Dickens' Village.")

DV86-1

CHRISTMAS CAROL COTTAGES:

FEZZIWIG'S WAREHOUSE

SCROOGE & MARLEY
COUNTING HOUSE

THE COTTAGE OF
BOB CRATCHIT & TINY TIM

DV86-2

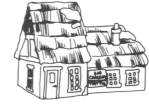

FEZZIWIG'S WAREHOUSE
Squared brick two story building with two brick chimneys. Second story front face is plaster over brick. Entire front is windowed.

DV86-3

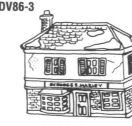

SCROOGE & MARLEY COUNTING HOUSE
Simple rectangular shape. Bottom brick, second story plastered with shuttered windows. Bay window major decorative design.

DV86-4

THE COTTAGE OF BOB CRATCHIT & TINY TIM
Small four room house, main room has fireplace for heat/cooking. Half of house rises two stories to provide sleeping area. Neatly thatched roof.

DV86-5

NORMAN CHURCH
Solid four-sided tower used as both watch and bell tower. Doors and windows reflect the Romanesque rounded arches.

DV86-6

DICKENS' LANE SHOPS:

THOMAS KERSEY COFFEE HOUSE

COTTAGE TOY SHOP

TUTTLE'S PUB

DV86-7

THOMAS KERSEY COFFEE HOUSE
Unique roof set upon simple rectangular building rises up to central chimney with four flue pipes. Brick, plaster, and timber with tile or slate roof. Large multi-paned windows predominate front walls.

DV86-8

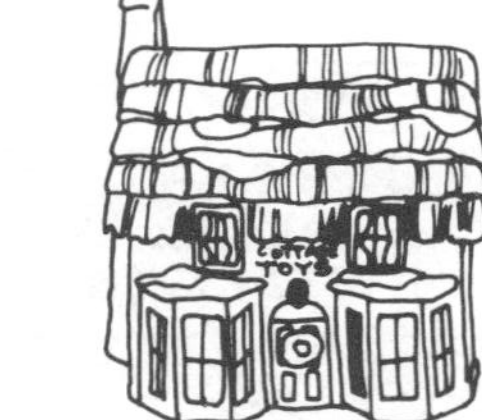

COTTAGE TOY SHOP
Small thatched roof cottage. Shop has large bay windows for light and display. Outside side stair/entry for family to living quarters.

ART CHART #	NAME	ITEM #	MATERIAL	SET?	💡	MARKET STATUS	ORIGINAL SRP	GREENBOOK TRUMKT PRICE
	VARIATIONS/MISC/COLLECTOR NOTES							
DV86-1	**CHRISTMAS CAROL COTTAGES**	**6500-5**	**Porcelain**	**SET OF 3**	✓	**CURRENT**	**$ 75.00**	**$ 90.00**
DV86-2	*FEZZIWIG'S WAREHOUSE*	6500-5	Porcelain	1 of 3 pc set	✓	CURRENT	25.00	30.00
	Early pieces have panes cut out of front door.							
DV86-3	*SCROOGE & MARLEY COUNTING HOUSE*	6500-5	Porcelain	1 of a 3 pc set	✓	CURRENT	25.00	30.00
DV86-4	*THE COTTAGE OF BOB CRATCHIT & TINY TIM*	6500-5	Porcelain	1 of a 3 pc set	✓	CURRENT	25.00	30.00
DV86-5	NORMAN CHURCH	6502-1	Porcelain	NO	✓	LTD. ED. 3,500	40.00	3000.00
	Early release to Gift Creations Concepts. Color variations: light to dark gray.							
DV86-6	**DICKENS' LANE SHOPS**	**6507-2**	**Porcelain**	**SET OF 3**	✓	**RETIRED 1989**	**80.00**	**595.00**
DV86-7	*THOMAS KERSEY COFFEE HOUSE*	6507-2	Porcelain	1 of a 3 pc set	✓	RETIRED 1989	27.00	165.00
DV86-8	*COTTAGE TOY SHOP*	6507-2	Porcelain	1 of a 3 pc set	✓	RETIRED 1989	27.00	225.00

DV86-9

TUTTLE'S PUB

Building rises three stories, ground level has pub for refreshments plus stable area for horse and carriages, second and third story jut out in step fashion. Travelers could rent rooms.

DV86-10

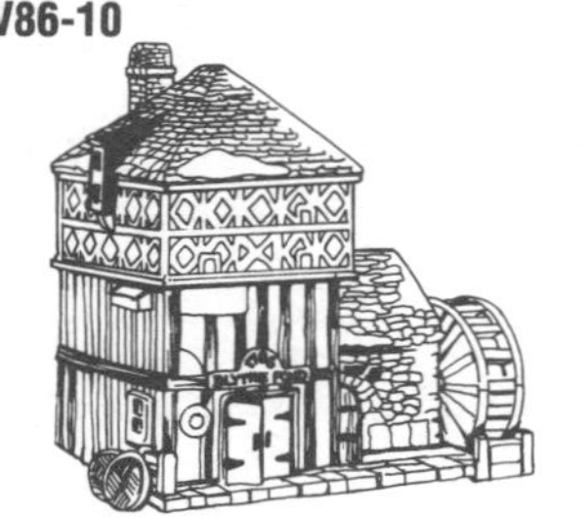

BLYTHE POND MILL HOUSE

Three story timbered house, rough stone wing connects water wheel. Grinding wheels rest alongside house, open front door.

DV86-11

CHADBURY STATION AND TRAIN

Three car train (engine, coal or wood car, and passenger car) and station built of irregularly shaped stone foundation and fieldstone. Columns support overhang keeping passengers dry. Indoor waiting area warmed by fireplace. Wooden benches provide rest area.

ART CHART #	NAME	ITEM #	MATERIAL	SET?	💡	MARKET STATUS	ORIGINAL SRP	GREENBOOK TRUMKT PRICE
	VARIATIONS/MISC/COLLECTOR NOTES							
DV86-9	*TUTTLE'S PUB*	6507-2	Porcelain	1 of a 3 pc set	✓	RETIRED 1989	$ 27.00	$ 225.00
DV86-10	BLYTHE POND MILL HOUSE	6508-0	Porcelain	NO	✓	RETIRED 1990	37.00	315.00
	Variation: "By The Pond" error on bottom @ $135.00. (Variation is more common than the correct piece and therefore is less expensive.)							
DV86-11	CHADBURY STATION AND TRAIN	6528-5	Porcelain	SET OF 4	✓	RETIRED 1989	65.00	375.00
	Variations in size.							

1987 THE HERITAGE VILLAGE COLLECTION – DICKENS' VILLAGE 1987

DV87-1

BARLEY BREE:

FARMHOUSE

BARN

DV87-2

FARMHOUSE

Thatched roof on small farmhouse with centralized chimney. Second story tucked into steeply pitched roof.

DV87-3

BARN

Stone foundation, thatched roof, for livestock.

DV87-4

THE OLD CURIOSITY SHOP

Corner shop for antiques is adjacent to rare book store. Curiosity building has large windows for display. Two chimneys. Book building is taller but narrower. Upper story window and roof dormer supported by wood ribs.

DV87-5

KENILWORTH CASTLE

Stronghold for Kings and Lords, began as a fortress and converted to Medieval Palace. Stone, thick walled, compact. Battlements surround all turrets.

DV87-6

BRICK ABBEY

Two spires flank front doors, rose window above entry oak doors. Example of a stage of Gothic architecture.

DV87-7

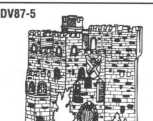

CHESTERTON MANOR HOUSE

Known as a Great House, set into countryside on acres of estate land. Stone facade, slate roof, area of plaster and half timber, open pediment above wood entry doors. Double roof peaks above central hall.

ART CHART #	NAME	ITEM #	MATERIAL	SET?	💡	MARKET STATUS	ORIGINAL SRP	GREENBOOK TRUMKT PRICE
	VARIATIONS/MISC/COLLECTOR NOTES							
DV87-1	**BARLEY BREE**	**5900-5**	**Porcelain**	**SET OF 2**	✓	**RETIRED 1989**	**$ 60.00**	**$ 395.00**
DV87-2	*FARMHOUSE*	5900-5	Porcelain	1 of 2 pc set	✓	RETIRED 1989	30.00	NE
DV87-3	*BARN*	5900-5	Porcelain	1 of a 2 pc set	✓	RETIRED 1989	30.00	NE
DV87-4	THE OLD CURIOSITY SHOP	5905-6	Porcelain	NO	✓	CURRENT	32.00	42.00
	Designed after the Old Curiosity Shop on Portsmouth Street in London.							
DV87-5	KENILWORTH CASTLE	5916-1	Porcelain	NO	✓	RETIRED 1988	70.00	675.00
	Variation: slight size changes over two years. Inspired by the remains of Kenilworth Castle in Warwickshire, England.							
DV87-6	BRICK ABBEY	6549-8	Porcelain	NO	✓	RETIRED 1989	33.00	395.00
DV87-7	CHESTERTON MANOR HOUSE	6568-4	Porcelain	NO	✓	LTD. ED. 7,500	45.00	1650.00
	Variations in color. Early release to Gift Creations Concepts.							

NE = NOT ESTABLISHED

1988 . . . THE HERITAGE VILLAGE COLLECTION – DICKENS' VILLAGE 1988 . . .

DV88-1

COUNTING HOUSE & SILAS THIMBLETON BARRISTER

Square, tall, 3 story, 3 chimney, offices. 4 equal gables create 4 section pitched roof. Attached plaster/timbered 3 story office is smaller and narrower.

DV88-2

C. FLETCHER PUBLIC HOUSE

5 windows shape corner of unique pub. 2nd story wider/longer, supported by wood ribs. Sweet Shop tucked in alongside pub is plaster/timbered design.

DV88-3

COBBLESTONE SHOPS:

THE WOOL SHOP

BOOTER AND COBBLER

T. WELLS FRUIT & SPICE SHOP

DV88-4

THE WOOL SHOP

Low turret rounds out one front corner of shop. Wood framing of three front windows and lattice design. Light by front door.

DV88-5

BOOTER AND COBBLER

Shoes made and repaired in this stone building with entry via Tannery where leather is cured and dyed. Outdoor light by main display window, wood hatch on roof opening.

DV88-6

T. WELLS FRUIT & SPICE SHOP

White washed brick and timbered building. Front window has stone ledge. Outdoor covered produce bin for food.

DV88-7

NICHOLAS NICKLEBY:

NICHOLAS NICKLEBY COTTAGE

WACKFORD SQUEERS BOARDING SCHOOL

DV88-8

NICHOLAS NICKLEBY COTTAGE

Brick, stone, and slate roofed home. Three chimneys, curved timbers decorate second floor. Bay window on front room. Two roof dormers.

ART CHART #	NAME	ITEM #	MATERIAL	SET?	!	MARKET STATUS	ORIGINAL SRP	GREENBOOK TRUMKT PRICE
	VARIATIONS/MISC/COLLECTOR NOTES							
DV88-1	COUNTING HOUSE & SILAS THIMBLETON BARRISTER	5902-1	Porcelain	NO	✓	RETIRED 1990	$ 32.00	$ 85.00
DV88-2	C. FLETCHER PUBLIC HOUSE	5904-8	Porcelain	NO	✓	LTD. ED. 12,500*	35.00	575.00
	*Plus Proof Editions. Market Price for Proofs is not established. Early release to Gift Creations Concepts.							
DV88-3	**COBBLESTONE SHOPS**	**5924-2**	**Porcelain**	**SET OF 3**	✓	**RETIRED 1990**	**95.00**	**365.00**
DV88-4	*THE WOOL SHOP*	5924-2	Porcelain	1 of a 3 pc set	✓	RETIRED 1990	32.00	180.00
DV88-5	*BOOTER AND COBBLER*	5924-2	Porcelain	1 of a 3 pc set	✓	RETIRED 1990	32.00	115.00
	Some sleeves have picture of T. Wells Fruit & Spice Shop on them.							
DV88-6	*T. WELLS FRUIT & SPICE SHOP*	5924-2	Porcelain	1 of a 3 pc set	✓	RETIRED 1990	32.00	95.00
	Some sleeves have picture of Booter And Cobbler on them.							
DV88-7	**NICHOLAS NICKLEBY**	**5925-0**	**Porcelain**	**SET OF 2**	✓	**RETIRED 1991**	**72.00**	**155.00**
	Variation: Set with Nic"k"olas Error @ $185.00.							
DV88-8	*NICHOLAS NICKLEBY COTTAGE*	5925-0	Porcelain	1 of a 2 pc set	✓	RETIRED 1991	36.00	80.00
	Variation: Nic"k"olas Error @ $100.							

. . . 1988 THE HERITAGE VILLAGE COLLECTION – DICKENS' VILLAGE . . . 1988

DV88-9

WACKFORD SQUEERS BOARDING SCHOOL

Three chimneys along ridge of steeply pitched roof w/many gables. Classrooms downstairs with student rooms above. Attic windows are shuttered.

DV88-10

MERCHANT SHOPS:

POULTERER
GEO. WEETON WATCHMAKER
THE MERMAID FISH SHOPPE
WHITE HORSE BAKERY
WALPOLE TAILORS

DV88-11

POULTERER

Three story stone block and timber, fresh geese hang outside front door.

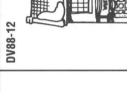

DV88-12

GEO. WEETON WATCHMAKER

All brick, rounded bay window, slate roof, fan light window in oak front door.

DV88-13

THE MERMAID FISH SHOPPE

Roadside fish bins, bay windows, angled doors and walls, wooden trap door in roof.

DV88-14

WHITE HORSE BAKERY

Two large windows to display baked goods, roof is hipped and gabled with scalloped shingles.

DV88-15

WALPOLE TAILORS

Stone and brick covered by stucco. Large first floor windows have wood panels under sills. 2nd floor has bow window.

DV88-16

IVY GLEN CHURCH

Square-toothed parapet tops stone turret by front entry of a thatched roof church. Curved timber design above door is repeated on bell chamber of turret. Arched windows. This church has a chimney.

ART CHART #	NAME	ITEM #	MATERIAL	SET?	!	MARKET STATUS	ORIGINAL SRP	GREENBOOK TRUMKT PRICE
	VARIATIONS/MISC/COLLECTOR NOTES							
DV88-9	*WACKFORD SQUEERS BOARDING SCHOOL*	5925-0	Porcelain	1 of a 2 pc set	✓	RETIRED 1991	$ 36.00	$ 85.00
DV88-10	**MERCHANT SHOPS**	**5926-9**	**Porcelain**	**SET OF 5**	✓	**RETIRED 1993**	**150.00**	**255.00**
DV88-11	*POULTERER*	5926-9	Porcelain	1 of a 5 pc set	✓	RETIRED 1993	32.50	55.00
DV88-12	*GEO. WEETON WATCHMAKER*	5926-9	Porcelain	1 of a 5 pc set	✓	RETIRED 1993	32.50	55.00
DV88-13	*THE MERMAID FISH SHOPPE*	5926-9	Porcelain	1 of a 5 pc set	✓	RETIRED 1993	32.50	65.00
DV88-14	*WHITE HORSE BAKERY*	5926-9	Porcelain	1 of a 5 pc set	✓	RETIRED 1993	32.50	55.00
DV88-15	*WALPOLE TAILORS*	5926-9	Porcelain	1 of a 5 pc set	✓	RETIRED 1993	32.50	55.00
DV88-16	IVY GLEN CHURCH	5927-7	Porcelain	NO	✓	RETIRED 1991	35.00	85.00

DV89-1

DAVID COPPERFIELD:

MR. WICKFIELD SOLICITOR
BETSY TROTWOOD'S COTTAGE
PEGGOTTY'S SEASIDE COTTAGE

DV89-2

MR. WICKFIELD SOLICITOR
Well-to-do legal practice and home. Second story has two balcony areas defined by low balustrades. 3 small dormers. Side door for family entry.

DV89-3

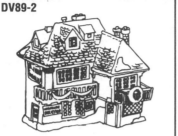

BETSY TROTWOOD'S COTTAGE
Country home – brick, timbered, whitewash. Two chimneys. Known for variations of wall angles. Roof ridge has unique dogtooth design.

DV89-4

PEGGOTTY'S SEASIDE COTTAGE
Up-side-down boat into a house, iron funnel as chimney, captains bridge, crows nest, barrels, boxes, ropes, and boots near entry.

DV89-5

VICTORIA STATION
Brownstone with granite pillars and facings – central section with domed red tile roof, two side wings, covered front drive-through, gold clock above entry.

DV89-6

KNOTTINGHILL CHURCH
Beige/honey stone with gray slate roof, arched windows. Turret bell chamber rises where church wings intersect.

DV89-7

COBLES POLICE STATION
Two story brick, stone outlines front entry and upper windows. Two watch turrets on 2nd story corners.

DV89-8

THEATRE ROYAL
Double set of doors fill theatre frontage. Garlands and gold bells add festive touch. Second floor rounded arch windows are separated by pilasters.

ART CHART #	NAME	ITEM #	MATERIAL	SET?	!	MARKET STATUS	ORIGINAL SRP	GREENBOOK TRUMKT PRICE
	VARIATIONS/MISC/COLLECTOR NOTES							
DV89-1	**DAVID COPPERFIELD**	**5550-6**	**Porcelain**	**SET OF 3**	✓	**RETIRED 1992**	**$ 125.00**	**$ 175.00**
	Variation: with "original tan" Peggotty's @ $225.00. Early release to Showcase Dealers, 1990.							
DV89-2	*MR. WICKFIELD SOLICITOR*	5550-6	Porcelain	1 of a 3 pc set	✓	RETIRED 1992	42.50	95.00
	Early release to Showcase Dealers, 1990.							
DV89-3	*BETSY TROTWOOD'S COTTAGE*	5550-6	Porcelain	1 of a 3 pc set	✓	RETIRED 1992	42.50	65.00
	Early release to Showcase Dealers, 1990.							
DV89-4	*PEGGOTTY'S SEASIDE COTTAGE*	5550-6	Porcelain	1 of a 3 pc set	✓	RETIRED 1992	42.50	60.00
	Variation: "original tan" @ $150.00. Early release to Showcase Dealers, 1990.							
DV89-5	VICTORIA STATION	5574-3	Porcelain	NO	✓	CURRENT	100.00	112.00
	Early release to Showcase Dealers and National Association Of Limited Edition Dealers, 1990. Designed after Victoria Station in London.							
DV89-6	KNOTTINGHILL CHURCH	5582-4	Porcelain	NO	✓	CURRENT	50.00	55.00
DV89-7	COBLES POLICE STATION	5583-2	Porcelain	NO	✓	RETIRED 1991	37.50	125.00
DV89-8	THEATRE ROYAL	5584-0	Porcelain	NO	✓	RETIRED 1992	45.00	80.00
	Inspired by the Theatre Royal in Rochester, England where Charles Dickens saw his first Shakespeare play.							

DV89-9

RUTH MARION SCOTCH WOOLENS

Herringbone brick design between timbers decorates front of one and a half story shops and home. Small flower shop tucked onto one side. Bay windows repeat diamond and hexagon panes.

DV89-10

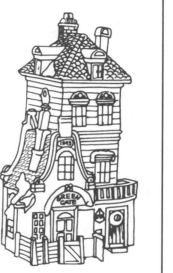

GREEN GATE COTTAGE

Three story home. Repeated vault design on chimney, dormers, and third story windows. Balcony above door. Fenced courtyard and two doors give impression of two homes. Small part has steep roof, crooked chimney, and ornamental molding.

DV89-11

THE FLAT OF EBENEZER SCROOGE

Four stories, broken balustrades and shutters, front door padlocked and chained, ghostly face on door knocker.

ART CHART #	NAME	ITEM #	MATERIAL	SET?	!	MARKET STATUS	ORIGINAL SRP	GREENBOOK TRUMKT PRICE
	VARIATIONS/MISC/COLLECTOR NOTES							
DV89-9	RUTH MARION SCOTCH WOOLENS	5585-9	Porcelain	NO	✓	LTD. ED. 17,500*	$ 65.00	$ 385.00
	*Plus Proof Editions. Market Price for Proofs is generally 10 to 20% less. Early release to GCC. Named for the wife of D56 artist, Neilan Lund.							
DV89-10	GREEN GATE COTTAGE	5586-7	Porcelain	NO	✓	LTD. ED. 22,500*	65.00	275.00
	*Plus Proof Editions. Market Price for Proofs is generally 10 to 20% less.							
DV89-11	THE FLAT OF EBENEZER SCROOGE	5587-5	Porcelain	NO	✓	CURRENT	37.50	See Below[1]
	Early release to National Association Of Limited Edition Dealers, 1989. Addition to "Christmas Carol" grouping. Variations affect TRUMARKET Price.							

[1] There are four variations of **The Flat Of Ebenezer Scrooge**:

a) 1st issue: made in Taiwan, has yellow panes in windows, far left shutter on 4th floor is slightly open to allow light to shine through - $100.00.
b) 2nd issue: made in Taiwan, no panes in windows - $60.00.
c) 3rd issue: made in Philippines, has yellow panes in windows, far left shutter on 4th floor is sealed - SRP @ $37.50.
d) 4th issue: made in China, has yellow panes in windows - SRP @ $37.50.

DV90-1

BISHOPS OAST HOUSE

Large attached barn, round cobblestone oasts contain a kiln for drying malt or hops to produce ale. Exterior finished as a rough-cast surface over brick.

DV90-2

KINGS ROAD:

TUTBURY PRINTER

C.H. WATT PHYSICIAN

DV90-3

TUTBURY PRINTER

Timbered/plaster design with decorative molding between first and second story. Ground floor bay window with smaller bays on second floor. Steeply pitched roof with a dormer.

DV90-4

C.H. WATT PHYSICIAN

Doctor's office on ground floor, outside staircase leads to family residence, bricks used above most windows as decorative arch, exposed stone edges on four corners of house walls.

ART CHART #	NAME	ITEM #	MATERIAL	SET?	💡	MARKET STATUS	ORIGINAL SRP	GREENBOOK TRUMKT PRICE
	VARIATIONS/MISC/COLLECTOR NOTES							
DV90-1	BISHOPS OAST HOUSE	5567-0	Porcelain	NO	✓	RETIRED 1992	$ 45.00	$ 75.00
DV90-2	**KINGS ROAD**	**5568-9**	**Porcelain**	**SET OF 2**	✓	**CURRENT**	**72.00**	**80.00**
DV90-3	*TUTBURY PRINTER*	5568-9	Porcelain	1 of a 2 pc set	✓	CURRENT	36.00	40.00
DV90-4	*C.H. WATT PHYSICIAN*	5568-9	Porcelain	1 of a 2 pc set	✓	CURRENT	36.00	40.00

DV91-1

FAGIN'S HIDE-A-WAY

Two attached buildings in disrepair. Broken shutters, cracks in wall. Barrel warehouse with steep roof, gate across doors.

DV91-2

OLIVER TWIST:

BROWNLOW HOUSE

MAYLIE COTTAGE

DV91-3

BROWNLOW HOUSE

Two story stone house with two brick chimneys and three front gables. Double doors.

DV91-4

MAYLIE COTTAGE

Pronounced roof ridge. Curved cone roof shape repeated on dormers and front door. One chimney rises up front facade, second chimney on side of house.

DV91-5

ASHBURY INN

Tudor timbered Inn for coach travelers. Food, lodging, and drink. Double chimneys, two roof dormers, and double peaks over multi-paned windows by entry.

DV91-6

NEPHEW FRED'S FLAT

Four story home with bow windows rising from second floor to roof like a turret. Planters flank front door. Side door with projecting window overhead and crowstepped coping in gable rising to two chimneys. Ivy grows up corner area - garlands, wreaths, and Christmas greetings decorate facade.

ART CHART #	NAME	ITEM #	MATERIAL	SET?	!	MARKET STATUS	ORIGINAL SRP	GREENBOOK TRUMKT PRICE
	VARIATIONS/MISC/COLLECTOR NOTES							
DV91-1	FAGIN'S HIDE-A-WAY	5552-2	Porcelain	NO	✓	CURRENT	$ 68.00	$ 72.00
DV91-2	**OLIVER TWIST**	**5553-0**	**Porcelain**	**SET OF 2**	✓	**RETIRED 1993**	**75.00**	**130.00**
DV91-3	*BROWNLOW HOUSE*	5553-0	Porcelain	1 of a 2 pc set	✓	RETIRED 1993	37.50	70.00
DV91-4	*MAYLIE COTTAGE*	5553-0	Porcelain	1 of a 2 pc set	✓	RETIRED 1993	37.50	65.00
DV91-5	ASHBURY INN	5555-7	Porcelain	NO	✓	CURRENT	55.00	60.00
DV91-6	NEPHEW FRED'S FLAT	5557-3	Porcelain	NO	✓	RETIRED 1994	35.00	65.00
	Addition to "Christmas Carol" grouping. Variation: Taiwan piece is darker in color and approx. 1/4" shorter than that from China.							

1992 THE HERITAGE VILLAGE COLLECTION – DICKENS' VILLAGE 1992

DV92-1

OLD MICHAELCHURCH

Stone base with lath and plaster filling space between timbered upper portion. Tower rises up front facade with heavy solid look, a simple four sided structure. Double wood doors at tower base. Chimney at rear of church.

DV92-2

CROWN & CRICKET INN

Three story brick and stone Inn. Pillars flank covered entry. Curved hood extends over Golden Lion Arms Pub on side. Wrought iron balustrade outlines front triple window on second floor. Dressed stone edges walls. Mansard roof with decorative edge trim and molding.

DV92-3

HEMBLETON PEWTERER

Timber framed with plasterwork panels in Elizabethan style. Bay windows frame out half the front facade. Chimney Sweep establishment with steeply roofed building hugs one side of the pewterer.

DV92-4

KING'S ROAD POST OFFICE

Simple four-sided stone three story building with semi circular turret-like two story rise out of window area. Entrance door surmounted by pediment just below post office sign. Triple flue chimney rises off back of building.

ART CHART #	NAME	ITEM #	MATERIAL	SET?	💡	MARKET STATUS	ORIGINAL SRP	GREENBOOK TRUMKT PRICE
	VARIATIONS/MISC/COLLECTOR NOTES							
DV92-1	OLD MICHAELCHURCH	5562-0	Porcelain	NO	✓	CURRENT	$ 42.00	$ 48.00
	Early release to Showcase Dealers and Gift Creations Concepts.							
DV92-2	CROWN & CRICKET INN	5750-9	Porcelain	NO	✓	1992 ANNUAL	100.00	175.00
	1st Edition in the Charles Dickens' Signature Series©. Special collector box and hang tag. Variation: light to dark trim.							
DV92-3	HEMBLETON PEWTERER	5800-9	Porcelain	NO	✓	CURRENT	72.00	72.00
	Variation: Early issue has two small additions on right side, latter issue has one larger addition.							
DV92-4	KING'S ROAD POST OFFICE	5801-7	Porcelain	NO	✓	CURRENT	45.00	45.00

1993 THE HERITAGE VILLAGE COLLECTION – DICKENS' VILLAGE 1993

DV93-1

THE PIED BULL INN

Elizabethan style with wood and plaster upper stories canterlevered out from stone and brick lower levels. Front entry at side of Inn allows public rooms to be of good size to service guests and local folk.

DV93-2

PUMP LANE SHOPPES:

BUMPSTEAD NYE CLOAKS & CANES
LOMAS LTD. MOLASSES
W.M. WHEAT CAKES & PUDDINGS

DV93-3

BUMPSTEAD NYE CLOAKS & CANES

Tall narrow shop with timbered 2nd story. Front gable has design etched into trim. Shop was noted for cloaks and capes as well as canes and walking sticks.

DV93-4

LOMAS LTD. MOLASSES

Steps lead up to store above stone lower level where molasses and treacles refined and stored. Double chimneys rise above thatched roof.

DV93-5

W.M. WHEAT CAKES & PUDDINGS

Baking chimney rises from center of main shop roof. 2nd story rooms are dormered with additional chimney at rear. Wreath hangs above curved front door and arched design is repeated above front windows.

DV93-6

BOARDING & LODGING SCHOOL

Attended by a young Scrooge, this red brick building combines a fortress-like solidity and elegant appearance based on symmetry of gables, coping, matching chimneys and rooftop balustrade cupola.

DV93-7

KINGSFORD'S BREW HOUSE

Stone 3 story building with slate roof processed grain into ales by fermentation. Chimneys rise from both sides from ovens & vats where the beverages were brewed. Banner of Tankard hangs outside.

DV93-8

GREAT DENTON MILL

Both grinding of grain for baking and animal feed as well as preparation of wool combed into yarn took place at Mill. Narrow 3 story wood structure with water wheel for power to turn wheels.

ART CHART #	NAME VARIATIONS/MISC/COLLECTOR NOTES	ITEM #	MATERIAL	◦SET?	!	MARKET STATUS	ORIGINAL SRP	GREENBOOK TRUMKT PRICE
DV93-1	THE PIED BULL INN	5751-7	Porcelain	NO	✓	1993 ANNUAL	$100.00	$ 145.00
	2nd Edition in the Charles Dickens' Signature Series©. Special collector box and hang tag.							
DV93-2	**PUMP LANE SHOPPES**	**5808-4**	**Porcelain**	**SET OF 3**	✓	**CURRENT**	**112.00**	**112.00**
DV93-3	*BUMPSTEAD NYE CLOAKS & CANES*	5808-4	Porcelain	1 of a 3 pc set	✓	CURRENT	37.50	37.50
DV93-4	*LOMAS LTD. MOLASSES*	5808-4	Porcelain	1 of a 3 pc set	✓	CURRENT	37.50	37.50
DV93-5	*W.M. WHEAT CAKES & PUDDINGS*	5808-4	Porcelain	1 of a 3 pc set	✓	CURRENT	37.50	37.50
DV93-6	BOARDING & LODGING SCHOOL (#18)	5809-2	Porcelain	NO	✓	1993 ANNUAL*	48.00	200.00
	*With Bottom Stamp of the Charles Dickens Heritage Foundation commemorating the 150th Anniversary of *A Christmas Carol*. Features #18 as address. Special box & hang tag. Also available from 1994 on as Item # 5810-6, without the commemorative stamp and an address of #43. Early release to Showcase Dealers and select buying groups.							
DV93-7	KINGSFORD'S BREW HOUSE	5811-4	Porcelain	NO	✓	CURRENT	45.00	45.00
DV93-8	GREAT DENTON MILL	5812-2	Porcelain	NO	✓	CURRENT	50.00	50.00

DV94-1

DV94-2

DEDLOCK ARMS

Stone wall courtyard has metal gate and 2 lanterns. 3 story Inn is brightly lit with Inn sign above front window.

DV94-3

BOARDING & LODGING SCHOOL

Attended by a young Scrooge, this red brick building combines a fortress-like solidity and elegant appearance based on symmetry of gables, coping, matching chimneys and rooftop balustrade cupola.

DV94-4

WHITTLESBOURNE CHURCH

Stone church with a single fortress-like tower rising off front right side. A masonry brace built against left side supports massive stone wall and provides a walkway.

DV94-5

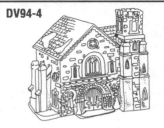

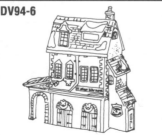

GIGGELSWICK MUTTON & HAM

Butcher shop concentrates on meats from sheep and pigs. Smokehouse on side cures meat and adds special flavoring. Shop has corner wraparound windows.

DV94-6

HATHER HARNESS

Stone, brick and stucco 3 story shop and family home. Double doors allow entry of horses, oxen, carriages and wagons to be fixed.

DV94-7

PORTOBELLO ROAD THATCHED COTTAGES:

MR. & MRS. PICKLE

COBB COTTAGE

BROWNING COTTAGE

DV94-8

MR. & MRS. PICKLE

Timbered stucco home with attached Antique Store. Home sign highlights a pickle.

ART CHART #	NAME	ITEM #	MATERIAL	SET?	!	MARKET STATUS	ORIGINAL SRP	GREENBOOK TRUMKT PRICE
	VARIATIONS/MISC/COLLECTOR NOTES							
DV94-1	DEDLOCK ARMS	5752-5	Porcelain	NO	✓	1994 ANNUAL	$ 100.00	$ 150.00
	3rd Edition in the Charles Dickens' Signature Series©. Special collector box and hang tag.							
DV94-2	DEDLOCK ARMS ORNAMENT	9872-8	Porcelain	NO		1994 ANNUAL	12.50	16.00
	Miniature version of the 1994 Annual above, packaged in a special keepsake box.							
DV94-3	BOARDING & LODGING SCHOOL (#43)	5810-6	Porcelain	NO	✓	CURRENT	48.00	48.00
	Features #43 as address. See 1993, #5809-2.							
DV94-4	WHITTLESBOURNE CHURCH	5821-1	Porcelain	NO	✓	CURRENT	85.00	85.00
	Midyear release.							
DV94-5	GIGGELSWICK MUTTON & HAM	5822-0	Porcelain	NO	✓	CURRENT	48.00	48.00
	Midyear release. Named after a town in North Yorkshire, England.							
DV94-6	HATHER HARNESS	5823-8	**Porcelain**	NO	✓	CURRENT	48.00	48.00
	Color variations in main part of shop/home.							
DV94-7	**PORTOBELLO ROAD THATCHED COTTAGES**	**5824-6**	Porcelain	**SET OF 3**	✓	**CURRENT**	**120.00**	**120.00**
DV94-8	*MR. & MRS. PICKLE*	5824-6	Porcelain	1 of a 3 pc set	✓	CURRENT	40.00	40.00

. . . 1994 THE HERITAGE VILLAGE COLLECTION – DICKENS' VILLAGE . . . 1994

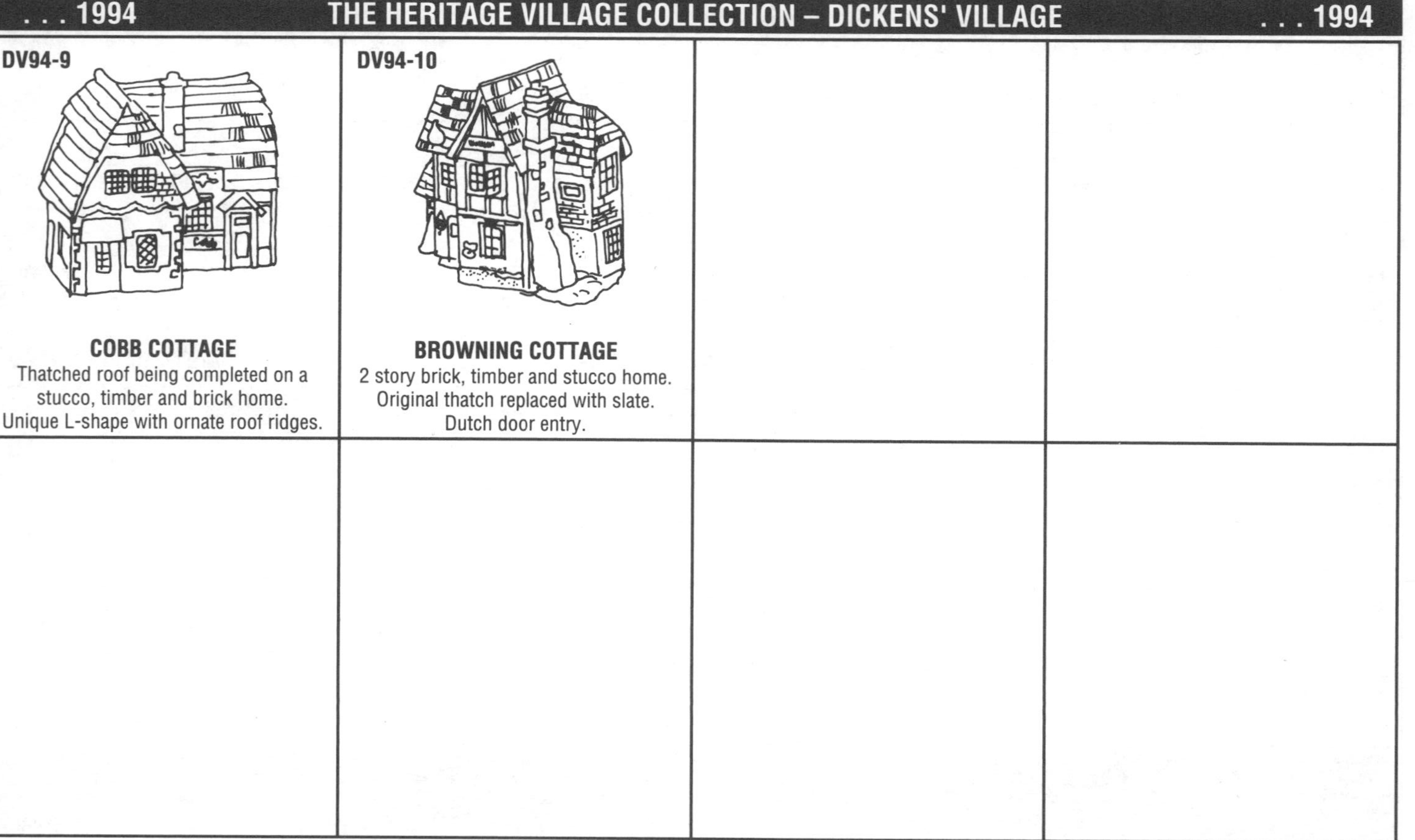

DV94-9

COBB COTTAGE

Thatched roof being completed on a stucco, timber and brick home. Unique L-shape with ornate roof ridges.

DV94-10

BROWNING COTTAGE

2 story brick, timber and stucco home. Original thatch replaced with slate. Dutch door entry.

ART CHART #	NAME	ITEM #	MATERIAL	SET?	!	MARKET STATUS	ORIGINAL SRP	GREENBOOK TRUMKT PRICE
	VARIATIONS/MISC/COLLECTOR NOTES							
DV94-9	*COBB COTTAGE*	5824-6	Porcelain	1 of a 3 pc set	✓	CURRENT	$ 40.00	$ 40.00
	First Heritage Village house without snow on the roof.							
DV94-10	*BROWNING COTTAGE*	5824-6	Porcelain	1 of a 3 pc set	✓	CURRENT	40.00	40.00
	As family wealth increased, home renovations included replacing original thatch with slate roof.							

DV95-1

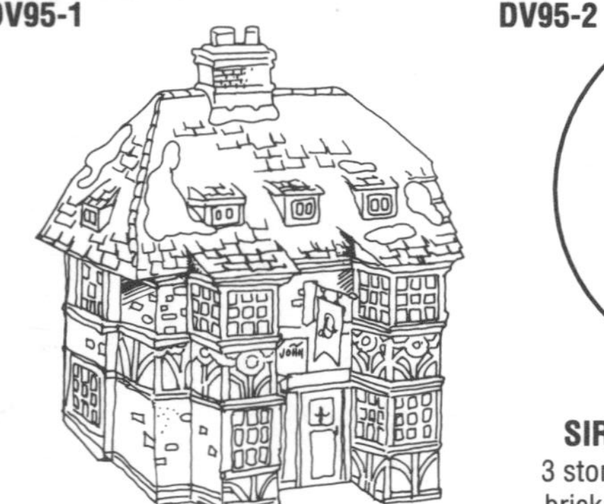

DV95-2

SIR JOHN FALSTAFF INN

3 story Inn of stucco, timber and brick with slate roof. 2 story bay windows frame front entry.

DV95-4

THE MALTINGS

Home, shop and bridge in one construct of stone, stucco and wood. Large doors allow carts to enter.

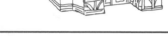

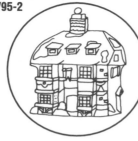

DV95-5

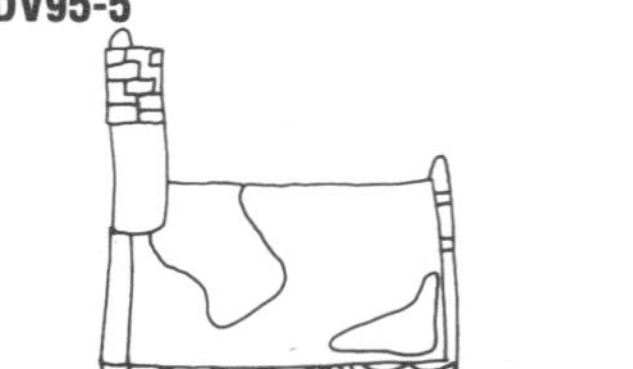

DUDDEN CROSS CHURCH

Brick church with stone coping. Bell tower rises on one side through roof. Stone archway to courtyard on other side near entry door.

DV95-3

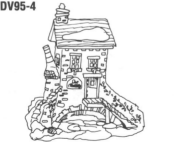

also includes:
Town Square Carolers accessory,
6 assorted sisal trees,
Cobblestone Road &
Bag of Real Plastic Snow

HOMES FOR THE HOLIDAYS:

FAVERSHAM LAMPS & OIL

2 story shop and home. Stone trim accents arched door and windows. Crowstepped trim on roof edges.

MORSTON STEAK AND KIDNEY PIE

Shop prepares a variety of meat pies in small 1-1/2 story building. Large many paned window by entry.

ART CHART #	NAME	ITEM #	MATERIAL	SET?	!	MARKET STATUS	ORIGINAL SRP	GREENBOOK TRUMKT PRICE
	VARIATIONS/MISC/COLLECTOR NOTES							
DV95-1	SIR JOHN FALSTAFF INN	5753-3	Porcelain	NO	✓	1995 ANNUAL	$ 100.00	$ 100.00
	4th Edition in the Charles Dickens' Signature Series©. Special collector box and hang tag.							
DV95-2	SIR JOHN FALSTAFF INN ORNAMENT	9870-1	Porcelain	NO		1995 ANNUAL	15.00	15.00
	Miniature version of the 1995 Annual above, packaged in a special keepsake box.							
DV95-3	HOMES FOR THE HOLIDAYS	5832-7	Porcelain	SET OF 13	✓	CURRENT	85.00	85.00
	Midyear release featured at D56 National Open House - Oct/Nov 1995. Special packaging for promotion.							
DV95-4	THE MALTINGS	5833-5	Porcelain	NO	✓	CURRENT	50.00	50.00
	Midyear release.							
DV95-5	DUDDEN CROSS CHURCH	5834-3	Porcelain	NO	✓	CURRENT	45.00	45.00
	Midyear release.							

continued from page 107

Q. *What does the phrase "the Big 3" mean? I have heard this term many times but have never been able to figure it out.*

A. "The Big 3" are the *Dickens' Village Mill, Norman Church* and *Chesterton Manor.*

At the time the term was coined these three buildings were the most limited and the most expensive pieces on the Secondary Market in The Heritage Village Collection. *The Cathedral Church Of St. Mark* with its unexpected closing at an edition limit of 3,024 pieces and the subsequent $2300.00 Secondary Market value has changed the rankings on both accounts.

Q. *At a recent Swap & Sell I saw a blacklight. I was told that I should have one if I plan to buy pieces on the Secondary Market.*

A. A blacklight is a useful tool because it illuminates glue, paint and other products used in the restoration process. If a piece has been restored, it will often alert you to this fact. Keep in mind most collectors and dealers are honest. Usually, repaired pieces are identified as such and priced to reflect their less than perfect status.

Q. *Every year I hear that there will be midyear retirements, but it never happens. Has there ever been a midyear retirement?*

A. No, there has never been a midyear retirement. This same rumor surfaces every year just before the announcement of the Midyear Releases in May. Many collectors, especially newer ones, get excited at the prospect.

Will there ever be? The only person with the answer to that question is the one who makes those decisions at Department 56. But don't forget, they have a habit of surprising us just when we think we have them figured out.

Isn't that great?

Q. *When will Department 56 produce another castle for Dickens' Village?*

A. I am asked this question quite often. New buildings are a very popular topic. It's impossible to predict when Department 56 will produce a particular type of building. If Department 56 produced all the pieces we ask for as soon as we ask for them, we would be buying lots of pieces each year. Besides, isn't anticipation much of the fun of collecting the villages? My suggestion is if you would like to see a certain type of building, write to D56 and tell them. Who knows, someday we may even see another castle.

Q. *What are your thoughts regarding the newer Department 56 pieces?*

A. I think the quality of design and craftsmanship is outstanding. In terms of design, there is no comparison between buildings that were issued even a few years ago to those that are being released today. The *Hunting Lodge* and *Fisherman's Nook Resort* have taken Snow Village to new heights in popularity. In Heritage Village, not only do the new pieces have more detail than the older ones, they also exhibit more imagination. Who would have thought we would ever see a Dickens' Village *Cobb Cottage* with its roof being repaired? Compare these pieces to the early ones. With better, more advanced, and sophisticated production capabilities, Department 56 can be more elaborate in design.

As for the overall production quality, I think it is much better that it was years ago. You may sometimes think otherwise, but did you inspect pieces so closely years ago? Most of us did not. We looked at the piece and if it wasn't cracked we bought it. Go back and inspect your older pieces as closely as you inspect your new pieces and you will see what I mean. On second thought, maybe you'd better not.

continued on page 172

NE86-1

NEW ENGLAND VILLAGE:

APOTHECARY SHOP
GENERAL STORE
NATHANIEL BINGHAM FABRICS
LIVERY STABLE & BOOT SHOP
STEEPLE CHURCH
BRICK TOWN HALL
RED SCHOOLHOUSE

NE86-2

APOTHECARY SHOP
Varigated fieldstone with white wood bay window. Gable and lean-to are blue clapboard.

NE86-3

GENERAL STORE
Round columns support full length covered porch. Two small dormers on roof with central chimney.

NE86-4

NATHANIEL BINGHAM FABRICS
Clapboard saltbox design fabric store and Post Office. Each shop has own chimney. Living quarters above larger fabric store.

NE86-5

LIVERY STABLE & BOOT SHOP
Two story painted clapboard house with wood planked wing contains tannery and livery stable. Stable has stone chimney, double doors.

NE86-6

STEEPLE CHURCH
White clapboard church w/tier 2 steeple. Windows have molding above and below. Simple design characteristic of area.

NE86-7

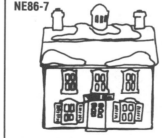

BRICK TOWN HALL
Mansard roof over two story Town Hall. Cupola is centered on roof ridge between two brick chimneys. Windows trimmed with ornamental molding.

NE86-8

RED SCHOOLHOUSE
Red wood school with stone chimney and open belfry. Hand powered water pump by front door.

ART CHART #	NAME	ITEM #	MATERIAL	SET?		MARKET STATUS	ORIGINAL SRP	GREENBOOK TRUMKT PRICE
	VARIATIONS/MISC/COLLECTOR NOTES							
NE86-1	**NEW ENGLAND VILLAGE**	**6530-7**	**Porcelain**	**SET OF 7**	✓	**RETIRED 1989**	**$ 170.00**	**$ 1250.00**
NE86-2	*APOTHECARY SHOP*	6530-7	Porcelain	1 of a 7 pc set	✓	RETIRED 1989	25.00	100.00
NE86-3	*GENERAL STORE*	6530-7	Porcelain	1 of a 7 pc set	✓	RETIRED 1989	25.00	350.00
NE86-4	*NATHANIEL BINGHAM FABRICS*	6530-7	Porcelain	1 of a 7 pc set	✓	RETIRED 1989	25.00	150.00
NE86-5	*LIVERY STABLE & BOOT SHOP*	6530-7	Porcelain	1 of a 7 pc set	✓	RETIRED 1989	25.00	145.00
NE86-6	*STEEPLE CHURCH*	6530-7	Porcelain	1 of a 7 pc set	✓	RETIRED 1989	25.00	See Below*
	Re-issued in 1989 as #6539-0 (NE89-4) when #6530-7 retired along with the other pieces of the NEV set. *For TRUMARKET Prices, see footnote[1] pg 145.							
NE86-7	*BRICK TOWN HALL*	6530-7	Porcelain	1 of a 7 pc set	✓	RETIRED 1989	25.00	210.00
NE86-8	*RED SCHOOLHOUSE*	6530-7	Porcelain	1 of a 7 pc set	✓	RETIRED 1989	25.00	260.00

NE86-9

JACOB ADAMS FARMHOUSE AND BARN

Red multi-level wood barn atop a stone foundation.
Stone silo attached. Home features front porch, small front bay window,
butter churn by door, simple design.

ART CHART #	NAME	ITEM #	MATERIAL	SET?	💡	MARKET STATUS	ORIGINAL SRP	GREENBOOK TRUMKT PRICE
	VARIATIONS/MISC/COLLECTOR NOTES							
NE86-9	JACOB ADAMS FARMHOUSE AND BARN	6538-2	Porcelain	SET OF 5	✓	RETIRED 1989	$ 65.00	$ 575.00

[1] **Steeple Church**:

a) 1st issue: part of NEV Original 7, #6530-7, tree attached with porcelain slip - $175.00.
b) 2nd issue: #6530-7, tree attached with glue - $100.00.
c) 3rd issue: Re-issue of church when Set of 7 retired, #6539-0, tree attached with glue - $85.00.

NE87-1

CRAGGY COVE LIGHTHOUSE

Keeper lives in small white clapboard home attached to lighthouse.
Front porch of home features holiday decorated columns.
Stone house foundation, whitewashed brick light tower.

NE87-2

WESTON TRAIN STATION

Luggage ramps lead to platform where you puchase tickets
and wait inside or on benches outside. Wheeled luggage cart stands on
side of building. White with blue trim and red roof.

NE87-3

SMYTHE WOOLEN MILL

Fabric woven for manufacture into clothing, yard goods.
Hydro powered by water wheel. Stone base with wood upper stories.
Bales of wool stacked outside office door. Lower windows each with shutter.

NE87-4

TIMBER KNOLL LOG CABIN

Two stone chimneys and fireplace provide heat and cooking facilities
for rustic log cabin, wood shakes comprise roof. One wing rises two stories.

ART CHART #	NAME	ITEM #	MATERIAL	SET?	!	MARKET STATUS	ORIGINAL SRP	GREENBOOK TRUMKT PRICE
	VARIATIONS/MISC/COLLECTOR NOTES							
NE87-1	CRAGGY COVE LIGHTHOUSE	5930-7	Porcelain	NO	✓	RETIRED 1994	$ 35.00	$ 60.00
	Early issue has drain hole directly below light tower, later issue does not.							
NE87-2	WESTON TRAIN STATION	5931-5	Porcelain	NO	✓	RETIRED 1989	42.00	275.00
NE87-3	SMYTHE WOOLEN MILL	6543-9	Porcelain	NO	✓	LTD. ED. 7,500	42.00	1150.00
NE87-4	TIMBER KNOLL LOG CABIN	6544-7	Porcelain	NO	✓	RETIRED 1990	28.00	165.00

NE88-1

OLD NORTH CHURCH

Red brick church. First and second floor windows feature sunburst and/or spoke tops. Steeple rises from main entry. Belfry has tiered design.

NE88-2

CHERRY LANE SHOPS:

BEN'S BARBERSHOP

OTIS HAYES BUTCHER SHOP

ANNE SHAW TOYS

NE88-3

BEN'S BARBERSHOP

A barber pole hangs from front house corner next to a bench for customers. Water tower on roof supplies the shop's needs. Upstairs office used by a lawyer.

NE88-4

OTIS HAYES BUTCHER SHOP

Dutch door entry, stone side walls, brick front. Small size and thick walls plus river/lake ice helped keep meat fresh.

NE88-5

ANNE SHAW TOYS

Large front windows with window boxes allow a look at toys for sale. Molding beneath roof edge and squared shape give roof a turret look/feel.

NE88-6

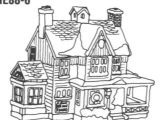

ADA'S BED AND BOARDING HOUSE

Large family home becomes a bed and breakfast for travelers. Double chimneys. Central cupola and wrap-around front porch.

ART CHART #	NAME / VARIATIONS/MISC/COLLECTOR NOTES	ITEM #	MATERIAL	SET?	!	MARKET STATUS	ORIGINAL SRP	GREENBOOK TRUMKT PRICE
NE88-1	OLD NORTH CHURCH	5932-3	Porcelain	NO	✓	CURRENT	$ 40.00	$ 45.00
	Based on Historic Landmark re: American Revolution and Paul Revere.							
NE88-2	**CHERRY LANE SHOPS**	**5939-0**	**Porcelain**	**SET OF 3**	✓	**RETIRED 1990**	**80.00**	**325.00**
NE88-3	*BEN'S BARBERSHOP*	5939-0	Porcelain	1 of a 3 pc set	✓	RETIRED 1990	27.00	95.00
NE88-4	*OTIS HAYES BUTCHER SHOP*	5939-0	Porcelain	1 of a 3 pc set	✓	RETIRED 1990	27.00	75.00
NE88-5	*ANNE SHAW TOYS*	5939-0	Porcelain	1 of a 3 pc set	✓	RETIRED 1990	27.00	160.00
NE88-6	ADA'S BED AND BOARDING HOUSE	5940-4	Porcelain	NO	✓	RETIRED 1991	36.00	See Below
	Color and mold variations affect TRUMARKET Price. See footnote[1] below.							

[1]**Ada's Bed And Boarding House**:

a) 1st issue: lemon yellow color, rear steps are part of building's mold, alternating yellow panes are in 2nd floor windows - $325.00.
b) 2nd issue: paler yellow, same mold - $150.00.
c) 3rd issue: pale yellow, stairs are added on, 2nd floor windows have yellow panes in top half of window only - $125.00.

NE89-1

BERKSHIRE HOUSE

Blue dutch colonial inn, two front entries, half porch, five dormered windows on front, second story mansard roof.

NE89-2

JANNES MULLET AMISH FARM HOUSE

White frame house, fenced yard on side, two chimneys, gutter and leader to barrel to collect rain water.

NE89-3

JANNES MULLET AMISH BARN

Wood and fieldstone with attached sheds and silo, Amish family black buggy stands at barn entrance.

NE89-4

STEEPLE CHURCH

White clapboard church with steeple. Windows have molding above and below. Simple design characteristic of area.

ART CHART #	NAME	ITEM #	MATERIAL	SET?	!	MARKET STATUS	ORIGINAL SRP	GREENBOOK TRUMKT PRICE
	VARIATIONS/MISC/COLLECTOR NOTES							
NE89-1	BERKSHIRE HOUSE	5942-0	Porcelain	NO	✓	RETIRED 1991	$ 40.00	See Below*
	*Variations in color affect TRUMARKET Price: "Original Blue" @ $150, "Teal" @ $100. "Forest Green" price is not established.							
NE89-2	JANNES MULLET AMISH FARM HOUSE	5943-9	Porcelain	NO	✓	RETIRED 1992	32.00	110.00
NE89-3	JANNES MULLET AMISH BARN	5944-7	Porcelain	NO	✓	RETIRED 1992	48.00	90.00
NE89-4	STEEPLE CHURCH	6539-0	Porcelain	NO	✓	RETIRED 1990	30.00	90.00
	Re-issue of 1986 Steeple Church #6530-7 (NE86-6). See footnote on page 145.							

NE90-1

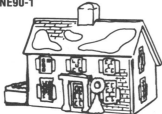

SHINGLE CREEK HOUSE

Saltbox design with chimney rising from mid-roof. Windows have shutters and molding on top and base. Attached shed on one side, with storm cellar doors and fenced side entrance.

NE90-2

CAPTAIN'S COTTAGE

2-1/2 story has balcony full length of 2nd story. Enclosed staircase on house side to second floor. A connected double dormer is centered on front roof between two ridge chimneys.

NE90-3

SLEEPY HOLLOW:

SLEEPY HOLLOW SCHOOL

VAN TASSEL MANOR

ICHABOD CRANE'S COTTAGE

NE90-4

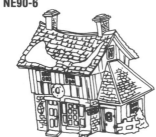

SLEEPY HOLLOW SCHOOL

Framed stone chimney warms log cabin school. Brick and wood belfry houses bell. Wood pile and bench with bucket near front door.

NE90-5

VAN TASSEL MANOR

Yellow house with mansard roof with two front dormers. Wood corner posts support porch. Stone lean-to one side. Double chimneys rise off roof ridge. Four ears of corn decorate front entry.

NE90-6

ICHABOD CRANE'S COTTAGE

Stone first story topped by wood second story. Rough shingled roof with dip in the middle between two brick chimneys.

NE90-7

SLEEPY HOLLOW CHURCH

Wood church with steeple rising off front. Arched windows with prominent sills. Front steps lead to double doors with ornate hinges and molding.

ART CHART #	NAME	ITEM #	MATERIAL	SET?	!	MARKET STATUS	ORIGINAL SRP	GREENBOOK TRUMKT PRICE
	VARIATIONS/MISC/COLLECTOR NOTES							
NE90-1	SHINGLE CREEK HOUSE	5946-3	Porcelain	NO	✓	RETIRED 1994	$ 37.50	$ 45.00
	Early release to Showcase Dealers and the National Association Of Limited Edition Dealers.							
NE90-2	CAPTAIN'S COTTAGE	5947-1	Porcelain	NO	✓	CURRENT	40.00	44.00
NE90-3	**SLEEPY HOLLOW**	**5954-4**	**Porcelain**	**SET OF 3**	✓	**RETIRED 1993**	**96.00**	**170.00**
NE90-4	*SLEEPY HOLLOW SCHOOL*	5954-4	Porcelain	1 of a 3 pc set	✓	RETIRED 1993	32.00	80.00
NE90-5	*VAN TASSEL MANOR*	5954-4	Porcelain	1 of a 3 pc set	✓	RETIRED 1993	32.00	60.00
NE90-6	*ICHABOD CRANE'S COTTAGE*	5954-4	Porcelain	1 of a 3 pc set	✓	RETIRED 1993	32.00	55.00
NE90-7	SLEEPY HOLLOW CHURCH	5955-2	Porcelain	NO	✓	RETIRED 1993	36.00	60.00

NE91-1

MCGREBE-CUTTERS & SLEIGHS

Builders of carriages, sleighs, and sleds to move people and goods in snowy New England. Stone and wood building. Large doors in front and side to allow movement of vehicles. Stone half has short tower atop roof. Large loft doors above entry.

ART CHART #	NAME	ITEM #	MATERIAL	SET?	!	MARKET STATUS	ORIGINAL SRP	GREENBOOK TRUMKT PRICE
	VARIATIONS/MISC/COLLECTOR NOTES							
NE91-1	MCGREBE-CUTTERS & SLEIGHS	5640-5	Porcelain	NO	✓	CURRENT	$ 45.00	$ 48.00

NE92-1

BLUEBIRD SEED AND BULB

Covered storage area near entry door has open storage bins.
Small shuttered arched window adjacent to door.
Outside stairs lead to other storage areas.
Two stories with stone block lower level and fieldstone chimney.

NE92-2

YANKEE JUD BELL CASTING

Red brick foundry with steeply pitched gable roof.
Projecting side doors on second and third story for lifting heavy, large castings. Tall circular brick chimney rises off rear of foundry.

NE92-3

STONEY BROOK TOWN HALL

Rectangular brick building serves as meeting hall for town governance.
Side entry with a latch gate, cellar windows with shutters, roof dormers and two chimneys, and many windows on long sides of building complete structure.

ART CHART #	NAME	ITEM #	MATERIAL	SET?	💡	MARKET STATUS	ORIGINAL SRP	GREENBOOK TRUMKT PRICE
	VARIATIONS/MISC/COLLECTOR NOTES							
NE92-1	BLUEBIRD SEED AND BULB	5642-1	Porcelain	NO	✓	CURRENT	$ 48.00	$ 48.00
NE92-2	YANKEE JUD BELL CASTING	5643-0	Porcelain	NO	✓	CURRENT	44.00	44.00
NE92-3	STONEY BROOK TOWN HALL	5644-8	Porcelain	NO	✓	CURRENT	42.00	42.00

NE93-1

BLUE STAR ICE CO.

Stone 1st story with insulated wood upper storage level. Wooden chute enabled ice blocks to be pulled up where sawdust or salt hay insulated each block.

NE93-2

A. BIELER FARM:

PENNSYLVANIA DUTCH FARMHOUSE
PENNSYLVANIA DUTCH BARN

NE93-3

PENNSYLVANIA DUTCH FARMHOUSE

Two story clapboard home. Many windowed to let in light, colorful trim on all windows, roof and wall moldings.

NE93-4

PENNSYLVANIA DUTCH BARN

Red barn with green mansard roof. Two stone silos on one corner. Double door entry reached by stone supported ramp. Hex signs hung on barn outer walls.

ART CHART #	NAME	ITEM #	MATERIAL	SET?	💡	MARKET STATUS	ORIGINAL SRP	GREENBOOK TRUMKT PRICE
	VARIATIONS/MISC/COLLECTOR NOTES							
NE93-1	BLUE STAR ICE CO.	5647-2	Porcelain	NO	✓	CURRENT	$ 45.00	$ 48.00
NE93-2	**A. BIELER FARM**	**5648-0**	**Porcelain**	**SET OF 2**	✓	**CURRENT**	**92.00**	**95.00**
NE93-3	*PENNSYLVANIA DUTCH FARMHOUSE*	5648-0	Porcelain	1 of a 2 pc set	✓	CURRENT	42.00	43.50
NE93-4	*PENNSYLVANIA DUTCH BARN*	5648-0	Porcelain	1 of a 2 pc set	✓	CURRENT	50.00	51.50

NE94-1

ARLINGTON FALLS CHURCH

Wood church with steeple rising in tiers above from entry. Pillars at front doors are wrapped in garlands. Double tier of windows on side of church to let in daylight. Simple structure with a country look.

NE94-2

CAPE KEAG FISH CANNERY

Lobster pots, buoys are stacked on wharf along building front. Brick tower rising on side of factory cannery puts focus on fishing and canning industry.

NE94-3

PIGEONHEAD LIGHTHOUSE

Light shines from porthole windows. Tower connects to keeper's home. Steps lead down from rocks to water.

ART CHART #	NAME	ITEM #	MATERIAL	SET?	!	MARKET STATUS	ORIGINAL SRP	GREENBOOK TRUMKT PRICE
	VARIATIONS/MISC/COLLECTOR NOTES							
NE94-1	ARLINGTON FALLS CHURCH	5651-0	Porcelain	NO	✓	CURRENT	$ 40.00	$ 42.00
	Midyear release.							
NE94-2	CAPE KEAG FISH CANNERY	5652-9	Porcelain	NO	✓	CURRENT	48.00	48.00
NE94-3	PIGEONHEAD LIGHTHOUSE	5653-7	Porcelain	NO	✓	CURRENT	50.00	50.00

1995 THE HERITAGE VILLAGE COLLECTION – NEW ENGLAND VILLAGE 1995

NE95-1	NE95-2	NE95-3	
BREWSTER BAY COTTAGES: JEREMIAH BREWSTER HOUSE THOMAS T. JULIAN HOUSE	**JEREMIAH BREWSTER HOUSE** Shed roof side addition attached to main square 2 story house. Shuttered windows, widow's walk on roof.	**THOMAS T. JULIAN HOUSE** Central chimney rises where 4 gabled roof meets. 2 story bay windowed turret next to covered porch entry.	

ART CHART #	NAME	ITEM #	MATERIAL	SET?	!	MARKET STATUS	ORIGINAL SRP	GREENBOOK TRUMKT PRICE
	VARIATIONS/MISC/COLLECTOR NOTES							
NE95-1	**BREWSTER BAY COTTAGES**	**5657-0**	**Porcelain**	**SET OF 2**	✓	**CURRENT**	**$ 90.00**	**$ 90.00**
	Midyear release.							
NE95-2	*JEREMIAH BREWSTER HOUSE*	5657-0	Porcelain	1 of a 2 pc set	✓	CURRENT	45.00	45.00
	Midyear release.							
NE95-3	*THOMAS T. JULIAN HOUSE*	5657-0	Porcelain	1 of a 2 pc set	✓	CURRENT	45.00	45.00
	Midyear release.							

1986 THE HERITAGE VILLAGE COLLECTION – ALPINE VILLAGE 1986

ALP86-1

ALPINE VILLAGE:

BESSOR BIERKELLER
GASTHOF EISL
APOTHEKE
E. STAUBR BACKER
MILCH-KASE

ALP86-2

BESSOR BIERKELLER

(BEER CELLAR)

Window boxes on second story hung with colorful banners. Third story rustic timbered enclosed balcony has garland decoration.

ALP86-3

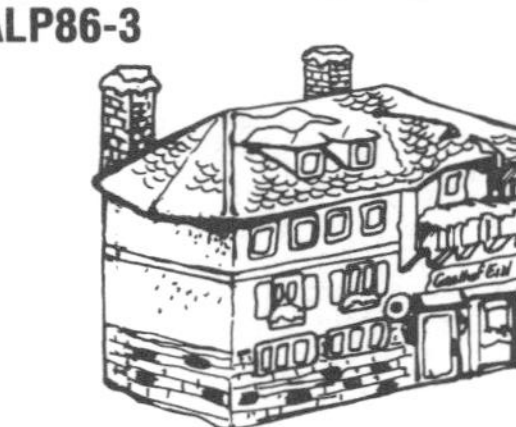

GASTHOF EISL

(GUEST HOUSE)

Rustic inn, fieldstone first floor with two stories of stucco topped by orange/red roof. A third story balcony is decorated with greenery and banners. Window boxes also decorate other rooms.

ALP86-4

APOTHEKE

(APOTHECARY)

Cream walls topped by blue roof. Banners flying from attic window. Prescriptions and drugstore supplies available from store on ground floor. Building shares with tobacconist.

ALP86-5

E. STAUBR BACKER

(BAKERY)

Three story building with bakery on ground level. Third story has some timbering design and an oriel window. Tiled roof and two chimneys.

ALP86-6

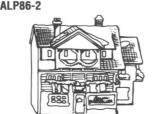

MILCH-KASE

(MILK & CHEESE SHOP)

Milk cans by door denotes shop that sells milk and cheese. Rough slate roof tops blue walls and wood planking exterior. Double wood doors allow wagons to bring supplies in/out.

ART CHART #	NAME	ITEM #	MATERIAL	SET?	💡	MARKET STATUS	ORIGINAL SRP	GREENBOOK TRUMKT PRICE
	VARIATIONS/MISC/COLLECTOR NOTES							
ALP86-1	**ALPINE VILLAGE**	**6540-4**	**Porcelain**	**SET OF 5**	✓	**CURRENT**	**$150.00**	**$195.00**
	Early release to National Association Of Limited Edition Dealers, 1987.							
ALP86-2	*BESSOR BIERKELLER (BEER CELLAR)*	6540-4	Porcelain	1 of a 5 pc set	✓	CURRENT	25.00	39.00
ALP86-3	*GASTHOF EISL (GUEST HOUSE)*	6540-4	Porcelain	1 of a 5 pc set	✓	CURRENT	25.00	39.00
ALP86-4	*APOTHEKE (APOTHECARY)*	6540-4	Porcelain	1 of a 5 pc set	✓	CURRENT	25.00	39.00
ALP86-5	*E. STAUBR BACKER (BAKERY)*	6540-4	Porcelain	1 of a 5 pc set	✓	CURRENT	25.00	39.00
	Only building in which bulb is inserted in the side.							
ALP86-6	*MILCH-KASE (MILK & CHEESE SHOP)*	6540-4	Porcelain	1 of a 5 pc set	✓	CURRENT	25.00	39.00

ALP87-1

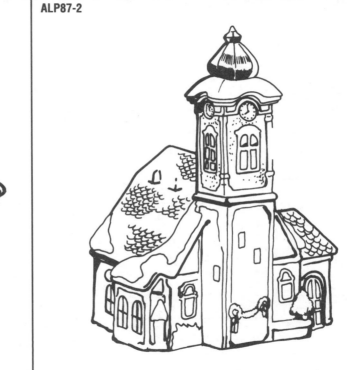

JOSEF ENGEL FARMHOUSE

House and barn are connected. Stucco over stone. Barn has hay loft above animal and equipment area. Shutters swing overhead. Home has balcony above front entry with herringbone planking. Red roof, capped chimneys.

ALP87-2

ALPINE CHURCH

Onion dome tops steeple which also features a clock on all sides of the tower.

ART CHART #	NAME	ITEM #	MATERIAL	SET?	!	MARKET STATUS	ORIGINAL SRP	GREENBOOK TRUMKT PRICE
	VARIATIONS/MISC/COLLECTOR NOTES							
ALP87-1	JOSEF ENGEL FARMHOUSE	5952-8	Porcelain	NO	✓	RETIRED 1989	$ 33.00	$ 975.00
ALP87-2	ALPINE CHURCH	6541-2	Porcelain	NO	✓	RETIRED 1991	32.00	See Below*
	*Variations in color affect TRUMARKET Price: "white trim" @ $295, "dark trim" @ $165.							

1988

ALP88-1

GRIST MILL

Irregular shingle roofing tops the mill that grinds corn and wheat into meal and flour.

1990

ALP90-1

BAHNHOF

(TRAIN STATION)

Stucco upper wall atop tiled lower wall. Ticket window in base of tower rises through roof and repeats tile design.

1991

ALP91-1

ST. NIKOLAUS KIRCHE

Bell tower rises above front entry, topped by onion dome.
Set-in rounded arched windows accent nave sides.
Pebble-dash finish on surface walls.
The home of the Christmas hymn "Silent Night, Holy Night."

ART CHART #	NAME	ITEM #	MATERIAL	SET?	💡	MARKET STATUS	ORIGINAL SRP	GREENBOOK TRUMKT PRICE
	VARIATIONS/MISC/COLLECTOR NOTES							

1988

ART CHART #	NAME	ITEM #	MATERIAL	SET?	💡	MARKET STATUS	ORIGINAL SRP	GREENBOOK TRUMKT PRICE
ALP88-1	GRIST MILL	5953-6	Porcelain	NO	✓	CURRENT	$ 42.00	$ 45.00

1990

ART CHART #	NAME	ITEM #	MATERIAL	SET?	💡	MARKET STATUS	ORIGINAL SRP	GREENBOOK TRUMKT PRICE
ALP90-1	BAHNHOF (TRAIN STATION)	5615-4	Porcelain	NO	✓	RETIRED 1993	$ 42.00	$ 70.00
	Variation: some have gilded trim, others have dull gold trim.							

1991

ART CHART #	NAME	ITEM #	MATERIAL	SET?	💡	MARKET STATUS	ORIGINAL SRP	GREENBOOK TRUMKT PRICE
ALP91-1	ST. NIKOLAUS KIRCHE	5617-0	Porcelain	NO	✓	CURRENT	$ 37.50	$ 37.50
	Designed after Church Of St. Nikola in Oberndorf, Austria.							

1992	ALP92-1 **ALPINE SHOPS:** METTERNICHE WURST KUKUCK UHREN	ALP92-2 **KUKUCK UHREN** (CLOCK SHOP) Franc Schiller displays his trademark clock on shop sign above recessed entry door. Small shop has Wood timbers that outline the stone, brick and stucco exterior.	ALP92-3 **METTERNICHE WURST** (SAUSAGE SHOP) Stucco over stone and brick with steeply pitched roof coming down to first floor on sides. Front facade framed by ornamentally curved coping.
1993	ALP93-1 **SPORT LADEN** Shop for skiing and winter sports equipment. Small shop tucked away on one side. Roof overhangs protect facade and chimneys are capped to keep out snow, ice and rain.	1994	ALP94-1 **KONDITOREI SCHOKOLADE** (BAKERY & CHOCOLATE SHOP) Garland and banners hang down fron the second story balcony. The extended eaves protect the building from heavy snows.

ART CHART #	NAME	ITEM #	MATERIAL	SET?	!	MARKET STATUS	ORIGINAL SRP	GREENBOOK TRUMKT PRICE
	VARIATIONS/MISC/COLLECTOR NOTES							

1992

ART CHART #	NAME	ITEM #	MATERIAL	SET?	!	MARKET STATUS	ORIGINAL SRP	GREENBOOK TRUMKT PRICE
ALP92-1	**ALPINE SHOPS**	**5618-9**	**Porcelain**	**SET OF 2**	✓	**CURRENT**	**$ 75.00**	**$ 75.00**
ALP92-2	*METTERNICHE WURST (SAUSAGE SHOP)*	5618-9	Porcelain	1 of a 2 pc set	✓	CURRENT	37.50	37.50
ALP92-3	*KUKUCK UHREN (CLOCK SHOP)*	5618-9	Porcelain	1 of a 2 pc set	✓	CURRENT	37.50	37.50

1993

ART CHART #	NAME	ITEM #	MATERIAL	SET?	!	MARKET STATUS	ORIGINAL SRP	GREENBOOK TRUMKT PRICE
ALP93-1	SPORT LADEN	5612-0	Porcelain	NO	✓	CURRENT	$ 50.00	$ 50.00

1994

ART CHART #	NAME	ITEM #	MATERIAL	SET?	!	MARKET STATUS	ORIGINAL SRP	GREENBOOK TRUMKT PRICE
ALP94-1	KONDITOREI SCHOKOLADE (BAKERY & CHOCOLATE SHOP)	5614-6	Porcelain	NO	✓	CURRENT	$ 37.50	$ 37.50

continued from page 141

Q. *What is your opinion regarding the increasing prices of the accessories?*

A. First, examine 1987 Heritage Village Collection accessories the *Shopkeepers* or *City Workers*. Each retailed at $15.00. Then compare them to 1993's *Visions Of A Christmas Past* with a suggested retail of $27.50. Although nearly twice the money, the newer pieces are more intricate, more detailed and more colorful. On top of all this, you have six years of inflation. Department 56 could probably produce pieces retailing for $15 to $20 but we'd be disappointed. Department 56 collectors want our accessories to keep pace with the quality and design of our buildings.

Q. *I am under the impression that Department 56 stated that the North Pole Collection would remain a "small" village, but that is certainly not the case. Am I wrong?*

A. I've heard many collectors refer to one statement or another attributed to Department 56. Most of the time, these statements are incorrect. Without Department 56 making a statement in the *Quarterly*, through authorized dealers or in the press, I would take everything "Department 56 said" with a grain of salt.

Q. *Why does Department 56 continue to produce so many churches? At this time there are four in Dickens' Village alone.*

A. Two reasons. 1. A Village is very seldom left without a church. This is so every collection may include a church without it being necessary for collectors to purchase one on the secondary market, and 2. There are church collectors - people who are not Department 56 collectors but who collect churches of all shapes, sizes and manufacturers.

Though D56 does not make as many schools as churches, this is another type of building that attracts non-D56 collectors. Fire stations are another.

Q. *Does adding window panes to a building reduce its value?*

A. How you add the window panes may change the value. If you permanently adhere any product to the building, be it windows, the acrylic icicles produced by D56, or any other addition, it will lower the value of the building. Some collectors affix such products to their buildings with temporary adhesives such as D56's Tacky Wax. This soft, pliable wax will hold small objects in place, yet is easily removable. Most importantly, it leaves no residue.

Q. *For years there was only one Village Gathering. Now there seem to be Gatherings everywhere.*

A. You're right. For a couple of years the only Gathering was the Bachman's Village Gathering. Then, in 1992, there were six D56 sponsored Gatherings. Thirteen Gatherings were sponsored by D56 in 1994. This year many stores are staging large events and calling them a Village Gathering.

Q. *Who sets Secondary Market prices?*

A. You do! Surprised?

The Secondary Market only exists because you buy pieces no longer available at Suggested Retail Price. You buy these pieces from another collector, either directly or through a dealer. The prices you pay reflect the availability of items. If something is in short supply and lots of collectors want it, the price rises. Conversely, large supplies mean lower prices.

continued on page 208

CIC87-1

SUTTON PLACE BROWNSTONES
Three multi-storied homes - attached via shared common walls. Three shops occupy semi-below ground level space. Attic dormer windows have iron grillwork.

CIC87-2

THE CATHEDRAL
Twin spires, early Gothic design, and decorated windows set this Cathedral apart. Stone church incorporates a fortress-like solidness.

CIC87-3

PALACE THEATRE
Mask of Comedy & Tragedy are bas-reliefs on brick building featuring Christmas Show of Nutcracker. Stage entrance on side of building.

CIC87-4

CHRISTMAS IN THE CITY:

TOY SHOP AND PET STORE
BAKERY
TOWER RESTAURANT

CIC87-5

TOY SHOP AND PET STORE
Side by side Pet Store and Toy Shop. Tucked in at side is Tailor Shop. Ground floor has extra high ceiling with half circle windows.

CIC87-6

BAKERY
Four story building with Bakery on first two levels. Iron grill work for safety and decor on smaller windows. Two different height chimneys.

CIC87-7

TOWER RESTAURANT
Multi-sided tower structure is integral part of residential building. Double door entry to restaurant/cafe. Iron grillwork on upper tower windows.

ART CHART #	NAME	ITEM #	MATERIAL	SET?	💡	MARKET STATUS	ORIGINAL SRP	GREENBOOK TRUMKT PRICE
	VARIATIONS/MISC/COLLECTOR NOTES							
CIC87-1	SUTTON PLACE BROWNSTONES	5961-7	Porcelain	NO	✓	RETIRED 1989	$ 80.00	$ 825.00
CIC87-2	THE CATHEDRAL	5962-5	Porcelain	NO	✓	RETIRED 1990	60.00	335.00
	Variations: 1st issue - smaller, darker, snow on sides of steps; 2nd issue - larger, lighter, no snow on steps.							
CIC87-3	PALACE THEATRE	5963-3	Porcelain	NO	✓	RETIRED 1989	45.00	925.00
	Variations: in size, paint trim and snow.							
CIC87-4	**CHRISTMAS IN THE CITY**	**6512-9**	**Porcelain**	**SET OF 3**	✓	**RETIRED 1990**	**112.00**	**475.00**
	Variations: all three buildings vary from dark to light colors.							
CIC87-5	*TOY SHOP AND PET STORE*	6512-9	Porcelain	1 of a 3 pc set	✓	RETIRED 1990	37.50	220.00
CIC87-6	*BAKERY*	6512-9	Porcelain	1 of a 3 pc set	✓	RETIRED 1990	37.50	95.00
CIC87-7	*TOWER RESTAURANT*	6512-9	Porcelain	1 of a 3 pc set	✓	RETIRED 1990	37.50	200.00

CIC88-1

CHOCOLATE SHOPPE

Paneled roof between first and second story extends to shop signs. Building over Chocolate Shoppe rises three stories plus attic. Above Brown Brothers Bookstore is one short story plus attic. Stone facade has heart panels at base while bookstore has sign and canopy over window.

CIC88-2

CITY HALL

Imposing fortress with four towers at corners plus repeat design on clock tower. Broad steps plus large columns establish entry doors. Stone arches accent first floor windows plus tower window. Planters with evergreens on either side of steps.

CIC88-3

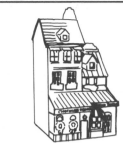

HANK'S MARKET

Grocery store as corner shop with boxes/barrels of produce on display. Rolled awnings over sign. Brick building with painted brick on upper sections of second story. Two upper windows are multi-paned with half-circle sunburst, other window has awning. Two chimneys on steeply pitched roof.

CIC88-4

VARIETY STORE

Corner store in two story brick building. Garland decorated awnings extend out to shelter display windows and shoppers. Separate door for upper story. Second floor corner window projects out as rounded tower and support column underneath becomes part of entry. Next door shop is barbershop with striped pole outside. Small eyeglass shop completes trio.

ART CHART #	NAME	ITEM #	MATERIAL	SET?	!	MARKET STATUS	ORIGINAL SRP	GREENBOOK TRUMKT PRICE
	VARIATIONS/MISC/COLLECTOR NOTES							
CIC88-1	CHOCOLATE SHOPPE	5968-4	Porcelain	NO	✓	RETIRED 1991	$ 40.00	$ 100.00
	Variations: varies from dark to light color.							
CIC88-2	CITY HALL	5969-2	Porcelain	NO	✓	RETIRED 1991	65.00	155.00
	Variation: smaller in size "Proof" version (none of the boxes had sleeves) @ $185.00.							
CIC88-3	HANK'S MARKET	5970-6	Porcelain	NO	✓	RETIRED 1992	40.00	80.00
	aka Corner Grocery.							
CIC88-4	VARIETY STORE	5972-2	Porcelain	NO	✓	RETIRED 1990	45.00	150.00
	Same mold as the Drugstore from the Bachman's Hometown Series, #672-6, (BHS88-1).							

CIC89-1

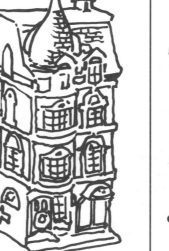

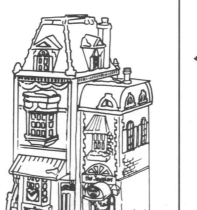

RITZ HOTEL

Red doors complete columned entryway, red window canopy over each second story French window. Stone, block, and brick building. Cupola on attic window. Slate roof.

CIC89-2

DOROTHY'S DRESS SHOP

Bright green door and awning, bay windows on first and second floor, mansard roof.

CIC89-3

5607 PARK AVENUE TOWNHOUSE

Four stories with ground floor card and gift shop, curved corner turret, blue canopy over double French door entry.

CIC89-4

5609 PARK AVENUE TOWNHOUSE

Four stories with ground floor art gallery, double wood doors lead to apartments, blue canopy over entry.

ART CHART #	NAME	ITEM #	MATERIAL	SET?	!	MARKET STATUS	ORIGINAL SRP	GREENBOOK TRUMKT PRICE
	VARIATIONS/MISC/COLLECTOR NOTES							
CIC89-1	RITZ HOTEL	5973-0	Porcelain	NO	✓	RETIRED 1994	$ 55.00	$ 65.00
CIC89-2	DOROTHY'S DRESS SHOP	5974-9	Porcelain	NO	✓	LTD. ED. 12,500	70.00	350.00
CIC89-3	5607 PARK AVENUE TOWNHOUSE	5977-3	Porcelain	NO	✓	RETIRED 1992	48.00	80.00
	Variation: earlier pieces have gilded trim at top of building, later production had dull gold colored paint.							
CIC89-4	5609 PARK AVENUE TOWNHOUSE	5978-1	Porcelain	NO	✓	RETIRED 1992	48.00	80.00
	Variation: earlier pieces have gilded trim at top of building, later production had dull gold colored paint.							

CIC90-1

RED BRICK FIRE STATION

Brick Station House for Hook & Ladder Company. Large wood doors lead to equipment with separate door for upper level. Stone block detailing on turret and above upper floor windows. Formal pediment at front gable.

CIC90-2

WONG'S IN CHINATOWN

Chinese restaurant and a laundry in brick building. Canopy over entry and at roof feature pagoda shape. Fire escape for second and third story tenants. Chinese characters highlight signs and entry.

ART CHART #	NAME	ITEM #	MATERIAL	SET?	!	MARKET STATUS	ORIGINAL SRP	GREENBOOK TRUMKT PRICE
	VARIATIONS/MISC/COLLECTOR NOTES							
CIC90-1	RED BRICK FIRE STATION	5536-0	Porcelain	NO	✓	CURRENT	$ 55.00	$ 55.00
CIC90-2	WONG'S IN CHINATOWN	5537-9	Porcelain	NO	✓	RETIRED 1994	55.00	70.00
	Variations: 1st issue - top window is red. 2nd issue - top window is gold.							

1991 THE HERITAGE VILLAGE COLLECTION – CHRISTMAS IN THE CITY 1991

CIC91-1

HOLLYDALE'S DEPARTMENT STORE

Corner curved front with awnings on windows, domed cupola, skylights on roof, and carved balustrade design on second story windows highlight store.

CIC91-2

"LITTLE ITALY" RISTORANTE

Three story tall, narrow, stucco finish upper level above brick street level entry. Outdoor cafe serving pizza is on side.

CIC91-3

ALL SAINTS CORNER CHURCH

Gothic style. Carved support frame arched windows, tall steeple with corners capped by small steeple design. Large windows exhibit tracery pattern.

CIC91-4

ARTS ACADEMY

Two story brick building has classrooms and practice halls. Curved canopy over entrance repeats design of arched triple window, skylight & small tower window.

CIC91-5

THE DOCTOR'S OFFICE

Four story brick building for Doctor, Dentist, and office space. Bow window is first level Doctor. Dentist windows have broad awning.

CIC91-6

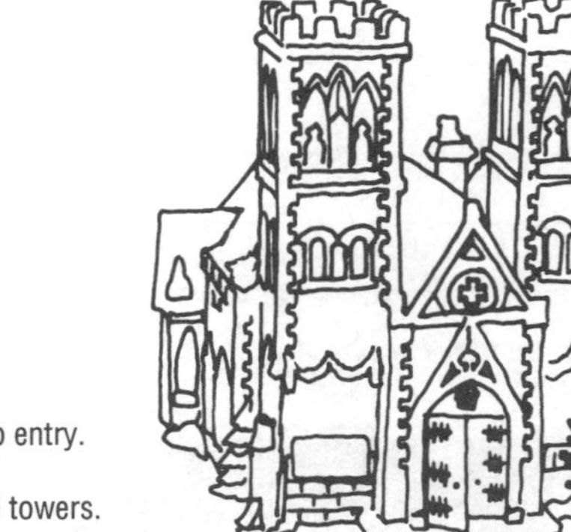

CATHEDRAL CHURCH OF ST. MARK

Front has look of fortification with two towers rising next to entry. Moldings are richly carved above double doors. Stone and brick with accented stone work framing walls and towers. Triple windows on each upper tower side.

ART CHART #	NAME	ITEM #	MATERIAL	SET?	!	MARKET STATUS	ORIGINAL SRP	GREENBOOK TRUMKT PRICE
	VARIATIONS/MISC/COLLECTOR NOTES							
CIC91-1	HOLLYDALE'S DEPARTMENT STORE	5534-4	Porcelain	NO	✓	CURRENT	$ 75.00	$ 85.00
	Variation: holly on canopies - 3 main entrance only vs. 2nd floor canopies as well.							
CIC91-2	"LITTLE ITALY" RISTORANTE	5538-7	Porcelain	NO	✓	CURRENT	50.00	52.00
CIC91-3	ALL SAINTS CORNER CHURCH	5542-5	Porcelain	NO	✓	CURRENT	96.00	110.00
CIC91-4	ARTS ACADEMY	5543-3	Porcelain	NO	✓	RETIRED 1993	45.00	75.00
CIC91-5	THE DOCTOR'S OFFICE	5544-1	Porcelain	NO	✓	RETIRED 1994	60.00	75.00
CIC91-6	CATHEDRAL CHURCH OF ST. MARK	5549-2	Porcelain	NO	✓	LTD. ED. 17,500*	120.00	2300.00
	Early release to Gift Creations Concepts, Fall 1992. *Closed at an announced 3,024 pieces due to production problems.							

CIC92-1

UPTOWN SHOPPES:

HABERDASHERY
CITY CLOCKWORKS
MUSIC EMPORIUM

CIC92-2

HABERDASHERY

Squared corner addition to three story building is entry for men's clothier. First floor front window topped by striped canopy and sign with store's name. Second floor triple windows topped by ornamental molding design and second floor side windows have triangular canopies. Brick, stone, and a roughcast pepple-dash facade construction.

CIC92-3

CITY CLOCKWORKS

Triangular shaped building with front angle blunted by semi-circular two story window treatment above entry to shop. Large clock hangs at right angles to store between sign and windows. Second clock next to entrance.

CIC92-4

MUSIC EMPORIUM

Andrew Alberts music store highlights a musical score on one side wall with a store sign superimposed and decorated for the holidays. Signs on the facade advertise a specialty in violins, flutes, with a horn design above one entry door. Tallest of the three shops, building rises to three floors plus attic dormer. Street level windows tall and narrow topped by sign. Predominantly brick.

ART CHART #	NAME	ITEM #	MATERIAL	SET?	!	MARKET STATUS	ORIGINAL SRP	GREENBOOK TRUMKT PRICE
	VARIATIONS/MISC/COLLECTOR NOTES							
CIC92-1	**UPTOWN SHOPPES**	**5531-0**	**Porcelain**	**SET OF 3**	✓	**CURRENT**	**$ 150.00**	**$ 150.00**
CIC92-2	*HABERDASHERY*	5531-0	Porcelain	1 of a 3 pc set	✓	CURRENT	40.00	40.00
CIC92-3	*CITY CLOCKWORKS*	5531-0	Porcelain	1 of a 3 pc set	✓	CURRENT	56.00	56.00
CIC92-4	*MUSIC EMPORIUM*	5531-0	Porcelain	1 of a 3 pc set	✓	CURRENT	54.00	54.00

CIC93-1

WEST VILLAGE SHOPS:

POTTER'S TEA SELLER
SPRING ST. COFFEE HOUSE

CIC93-2

POTTER'S TEA SELLER

Stone 3 story shop sells tea or serves tea by the cup. Stone arches decorate windows. Green awning covers upper window above entry. Sign hangs in front of door to alert shoppers.

CIC93-3

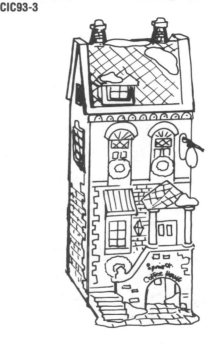

SPRING ST. COFFEE HOUSE

Four story narrow building. Steps to main level lead to entry door covered by small pillared portico. Coffee ground to order & blended for taste plus an area for having a cup. Brick lower level topped by stucco upper story.

ART CHART #	NAME	ITEM #	MATERIAL	SET?		MARKET STATUS	ORIGINAL SRP	GREENBOOK TRUMKT PRICE
	VARIATIONS/MISC/COLLECTOR NOTES							
CIC93-1	**WEST VILLAGE SHOPS**	**5880-7**	**Porcelain**	**SET OF 2**	✓	**CURRENT**	**$ 90.00**	**$ 90.00**
CIC93-2	*POTTER'S TEA SELLER*	5880-7	Porcelain	1 of a 2 pc set	✓	CURRENT	45.00	45.00
CIC93-3	*SPRING ST. COFFEE HOUSE*	5880-7	Porcelain	1 of a 2 pc set	✓	CURRENT	45.00	45.00

CIC94-1

BROKERAGE HOUSE

Three story stone building gives impression of invincibility. Four pillars support large entry pediment which has name of Exchange carved into stone. Feeling of wealth is reinforced by gold embellishments.

CIC94-2

FIRST METROPOLITAN BANK

Domed, 3 story building presents solid structure. 4 columns reach to third story and create covered entry and area for name inscription. Bank has gilt trim on dome, windows and door.

CIC94-3

HERITAGE MUSEUM OF ART

A stately, symmetrical structure with large windows. Names of famous artists are displayed around the top of the building and Thomas Nast's rendition of Santa Claus is on display above the entrance.

ART CHART #	NAME	ITEM #	MATERIAL	SET?	💡	MARKET STATUS	ORIGINAL SRP	GREENBOOK TRUMKT PRICE
	VARIATIONS/MISC/COLLECTOR NOTES							
CIC94-1	BROKERAGE HOUSE	5881-5	Porcelain	NO	✓	CURRENT	$ 48.00	$ 48.00
	"18" is symbolic of initial D56 stock offering at $18.00.							
CIC94-2	FIRST METROPOLITAN BANK	5882-3	Porcelain	NO	✓	CURRENT	60.00	60.00
CIC94-3	HERITAGE MUSEUM OF ART	5883-1	Porcelain	NO	✓	CURRENT	96.00	96.00

1995 THE HERITAGE VILLAGE COLLECTION – CHRISTMAS IN THE CITY 1995

CIC95-1

IVY TERRACE APPARTMENTS
3 story brick building with two canopy covered entries. 3rd floor apartment has terrace with wrought iron enclosure.

ART CHART #	NAME	ITEM #	MATERIAL	SET?	💡	MARKET STATUS	ORIGINAL SRP	GREENBOOK TRUMKT PRICE
	VARIATIONS/MISC/COLLECTOR NOTES							
CIC95-1	IVY TERRACE APARTMENTS	5887-4	Porcelain	NO	✓	CURRENT	$ 60.00	$ 60.00
	Midyear release.							

LTB87-1

LITTLE TOWN OF BETHLEHEM

Replica of Holy Family Manger Scene with Three Wise Men and Shepherd.
Stone and sun-dried brick homes and shelters add Mid-East simplicity. Animals attentive to Holy Family.

ART CHART #	NAME	ITEM #	MATERIAL	SET?	💡	MARKET STATUS	ORIGINAL SRP	GREENBOOK TRUMKT PRICE
	VARIATIONS/MISC/COLLECTOR NOTES							
LTB87-1	LITTLE TOWN OF BETHLEHEM	5975-7	Porcelain	SET OF 12	✓	CURRENT	$ 150.00	$ 150.00
	Variation: with and without snow on manger.							

NP90-1

SANTA'S WORKSHOP

Multi-chimnied, many gabled home and workshop. Stone foundation with stucco and timber upper stories. Balconies extend off windows and hold garlands. Mailbox by front door.

NP90-2

NORTH POLE:

REINDEER BARN

ELF BUNKHOUSE

NP90-3

REINDEER BARN

Stone and stucco has stalls for all reindeer. Steeply pitched roof has cupola on ridge and step design on front of dormers. Roof vents and dutch stall doors provide ventilation.

NP90-4

ELF BUNKHOUSE

Home for Santa's helpers, three stories with steeply pitched roof and protected chimney. Made of wood, stone, and stucco featuring bay windows, dormers, and a balcony.

ART CHART #	NAME	ITEM #	MATERIAL	SET?	!	MARKET STATUS	ORIGINAL SRP	GREENBOOK TRUMKT PRICE
	VARIATIONS/MISC/COLLECTOR NOTES							
NP90-1	SANTA'S WORKSHOP	5600-6	Porcelain	NO	✓	RETIRED 1993	$ 72.00	$ 375.00
NP90-2	**NORTH POLE**	**5601-4**	**Porcelain**	**SET OF 2**	✓	**CURRENT**	**70.00**	**80.00**
NP90-3	*REINDEER BARN*	5601-4	Porcelain	1 of a 2 pc set	✓	CURRENT	35.00	40.00
	Common variation: a name duplicated, another omitted on reindeer stalls.							
NP90-4	*ELF BUNKHOUSE*	5601-4	Porcelain	1 of a 2 pc set	✓	CURRENT	35.00	40.00

NP91-1

NEENEE'S DOLLS AND TOYS

Rough finish stucco and stone house. Steeply pitched rear roof, red shuttered lattice-paned front second story windows, monogram within wreaths.

NP91-2

NORTH POLE SHOPS:

ORLY'S BELL & HARNESS SUPPLY

RIMPY'S BAKERY

NP91-3

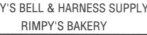

ORLY'S BELL & HARNESS SUPPLY

Stone steps lead to bell shop doorway with brick work design to frame it. Sleigh strap with bells above sign. Harness area has large wood doors that open to allow horse drawn carriage or wagon to enter. Window with balcony above, on 2nd story.

NP91-4

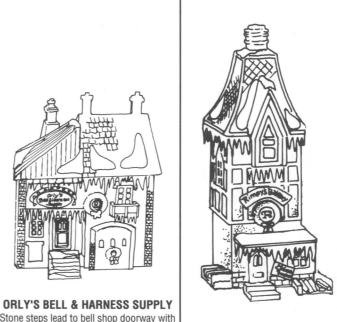

RIMPY'S BAKERY

Three storied, half wood timbered narrow building. Hipped - roof with gable on facade. Large eight paned front window with wood crib in front and on side.

NP91-5

TASSY'S MITTENS & HASSEL'S WOOLIES

Two shops in connected buildings. Hassel's has corner turret window and oriel turret upper window. Tassy's has angled front window at ground and three arched windows on overhang second story. Gable has carved bough and berry design - roof angles steeply pitched.

ART CHART #	NAME	ITEM #	MATERIAL	SET?	!	MARKET STATUS	ORIGINAL SRP	GREENBOOK TRUMKT PRICE
	VARIATIONS/MISC/COLLECTOR NOTES							
NP91-1	NEENEE'S DOLLS AND TOYS	5620-0	Porcelain	NO	✓	CURRENT	$ 36.00	$ 37.50
	Early release to Showcase Dealers and Gift Creations Concepts.							
NP91-2	**NORTH POLE SHOPS**	**5621-9**	**Porcelain**	**SET OF 2**	✓	**CURRENT**	**75.00**	**75.00**
NP91-3	*ORLY'S BELL & HARNESS SUPPLY*	5621-9	Porcelain	1 of a 2 pc set	✓	CURRENT	37.50	37.50
NP91-4	*RIMPY'S BAKERY*	5621-9	Porcelain	1 of a 2 pc set	✓	CURRENT	37.50	37.50
NP91-5	TASSY'S MITTENS & HASSEL'S WOOLIES	5622-7	Porcelain	NO	✓	CURRENT	50.00	50.00

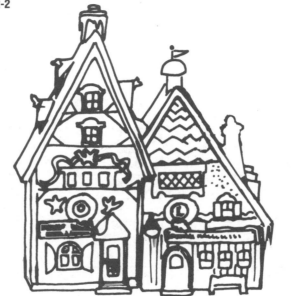

NP92-1

POST OFFICE

Basis for building is turret with what appears to be a half-house on one side of main tower. Second floor features multi-paned windows, small curved turret between second and third floor could hold staircase and take up little wall space. Third floor has low balcony outside windows.

NP92-2

OBBIE'S BOOKS & LETRINKA'S CANDY

The tall narrow books and toys shop contrasts sharply with the shorter, wider, candy shop. Both shops have steep pitched roofs. A bay window on Obbie's side wall plus a number of dormer windows reinforce the angular look of the shop. Onion dome shaped chimney and cupola on roof ridge are unique to Letrinka's which also has a vertical timbered ground level design. Both shops have lettered wreaths by front entries.

NP92-3

ELFIE'S SLEDS & SKATES

Distinctive roof design with chimneys that are only visible outside from the second story. Roof hood projects out from walls to protect windows on house sides as well as sweeping down to help form large front window. Wreath with letter "E" in addition to shop signs.

ART CHART #	NAME	ITEM #	MATERIAL	SET?	💡	MARKET STATUS	ORIGINAL SRP	GREENBOOK TRUMKT PRICE
	VARIATIONS/MISC/COLLECTOR NOTES							
NP92-1	POST OFFICE	5623-5	Porcelain	NO	✓	CURRENT	$ 45.00	$ 50.00
	Early release to Showcase Dealers.							
NP92-2	OBBIE'S BOOKS & LETRINKA'S CANDY	5624-3	Porcelain	NO	✓	CURRENT	70.00	70.00
NP92-3	ELFIE'S SLEDS & SKATES	5625-1	Porcelain	NO	✓	CURRENT	48.00	48.00

1993 THE HERITAGE VILLAGE COLLECTION – NORTH POLE 1993

NP93-1

NORTH POLE CHAPEL

Spire, containing brass bell rises at rear of Chapel. Fieldstone topped by timbered upper story. Double door front entry flanked by evergreens. Side chimney rises through roof with flue pipe capped by onion cap. Large wreath circled clock above entry.

NP93-2

NORTH POLE EXPRESS DEPOT

Receiving area for all people and deliveries into and out of North Pole not going by Santa's sled. Roof line at lowest point is pagoda-like with an A-frame gable transversing a ridge. Stone chimney rises from rear of roof. Passenger door as well as freight doors.

NP93-3

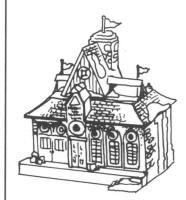

SANTA'S WOODWORKS

Lower level contains heavy equipment for sawing, debarking and trimming wood. Main woodworks level reached by wood stairs at side of open porch. Structure is a log house.

NP93-4

SANTA'S LOOKOUT TOWER

Pennants fly above door and top of tower which rises above trees to give Santa a clear picture of flight conditions. Balcony around highest story lets Santa check wind velocity.

ART CHART #	NAME	ITEM #	MATERIAL	SET?	!	MARKET STATUS	ORIGINAL SRP	GREENBOOK TRUMKT PRICE
	VARIATIONS/MISC/COLLECTOR NOTES							
NP93-1	NORTH POLE CHAPEL	5626-0	Porcelain	NO	✓	CURRENT	$ 45.00	$ 45.00
	Early release to Showcase Dealers and select buying groups.							
NP93-2	NORTH POLE EXPRESS DEPOT	5627-8	Porcelain	NO	✓	CURRENT	48.00	48.00
NP93-3	SANTA'S WOODWORKS	5628-6	Porcelain	NO	✓	CURRENT	42.00	45.00
NP93-4	SANTA'S LOOKOUT TOWER	5629-4	Porcelain	NO	✓	CURRENT	45.00	48.00

NP94-1

ELFIN SNOW CONE WORKS
Snow cones on shutters and sign of steep roofed shop. Roof molding trim resembles icing. Oriole window extends from 3rd floor to rooftop.

NP94-2

BEARD BARBER SHOP
Small shop with 3 tall front windows allowing light to enter. Barber pole at entry and banner of shears establish function of shop.

NP94-3

NORTH POLE DOLLS & SANTA'S BEAR WORKS
Two 3 story mirror image buildings with 2 story center connecting entrance way. Shops have doors by signs.
A "NP" pennant flies from the cupola in the center.

ART CHART #	NAME	ITEM #	MATERIAL	SET?	💡	MARKET STATUS	ORIGINAL SRP	GREENBOOK TRUMKT PRICE
	VARIATIONS/MISC/COLLECTOR NOTES							
NP94-1	ELFIN SNOW CONE WORKS	5633-2	Porcelain	NO	✓	CURRENT	$ 40.00	$ 40.00
NP94-2	BEARD BARBER SHOP	5634-0	Porcelain	NO	✓	CURRENT	27.50	27.50
NP94-3	NORTH POLE DOLLS & SANTA'S BEAR WORKS	5635-9	Porcelain	SET OF 3	✓	CURRENT	96.00	96.00
	Entrance is non-lit. Set of 3 consists of North Pole Dolls, Santa's Bear Works and Entrance.							

NP95-1

TIN SOLDIER SHOP

Tall, narrow shop with garland draped balcony. Toy soldiers decorate base of 2 story turret at side of entry.

ART CHART #	NAME	ITEM #	MATERIAL	SET?	!	MARKET STATUS	ORIGINAL SRP	GREENBOOK TRUMKT PRICE
	VARIATIONS/MISC/COLLECTOR NOTES							
NP95-1	TOY SOLDIER SHOP	5638-3	Porcelain	NO	✓	CURRENT	$ 42.00	$ 42.00
	Midyear release.							

DPV94-1

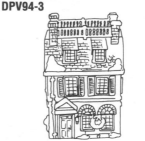

MICKEY'S CHRISTMAS CAROL

Replica of the building in Fantasyland in Disney World in Orlando, Florida. Gold trim and blue roof along with multiple turrets and gables make this a very distinctive building.

DPV94-2

OLDE WORLD ANTIQUE SHOPS

OLDE WORLD ANTIQUES I
OLDE WORLD ANTIQUES II

DPV94-3

OLDE WORLD ANTIQUES I

Similar building can be seen in Disney World's Liberty Square. Windows vary from arched to rectangular.

DPV94-4

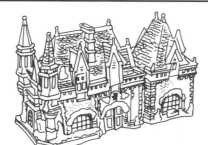

OLDE WORLD ANTIQUES II

Replica of the building in Liberty Square in Orlando's Disney World. Long staircase in front leads to second floor.

DPV94-5

DISNEYLAND FIRE DEPARTMENT #105

Inspired by the fire station on Main Street in Disneyland. Brick station's large front doors allow fire equipment in and out.

ART CHART #	NAME	ITEM #	MATERIAL	SET?	!	MARKET STATUS	ORIGINAL SRP	GREENBOOK TRUMKT PRICE
	VARIATIONS/MISC/COLLECTOR NOTES							
DVP94-1	MICKEY'S CHRISTMAS CAROL	5350-3	Porcelain	SET OF 2	✓	CURRENT	$ 144.00	$ 144.00
	#742-0 is an exclusive for Disney Theme Parks and has the "Holiday Collection" stamp.							
DVP94-2	**OLDE WORLD ANTIQUES SHOPS**	**5351-1**	**Porcelain**	**SET OF 2**	✓	**CURRENT**	**90.00**	**90.00**
	#743-9 is an exclusive for Disney Theme Parks and has the "Holiday Collection" stamp.							
DVP94-3	*OLDE WORLD ANTIQUES I*	5351-1	Porcelain	1 of a 2 pc set	✓	CURRENT	45.00	45.00
DVP94-4	*OLDE WORLD ANTIQUES II*	5351-1	Porcelain	1 of a 2 pc set	✓	CURRENT	45.00	45.00
DVP94-5	DISNEYLAND FIRE DEPARTMENT #105	5352-0	Porcelain	NO	✓	CURRENT	45.00	45.00
	#744-7 is an exclusive for Disney Theme Parks and has the "Holiday Collection" stamp.							

With the exception of the smaller piece of Mickey's Christmas Carol, The Disney Park Village buildings sold through the two Disney Theme Parks have the "Holiday Collection" bottom stamp on them.

At the time of introduction the number of pieces that would have the Holiday Collection bottom stamp was believed to be extremely limited. This belief created an almost immediate secondary market. As of this printing, however, Disney has decided to extend the length of time they will sell these buildings. Since this makes these pieces "current", we are not printing a secondary market value.

Buildings sold through Department 56 authorized dealers have "DVP" stamped on the bottom.

continued from page 173

Q. *What about boxes. Are they necessary or a necessary evil?*

A. You are the only one who can determine if the box is 'worth it."

More accurately, the answer depends on the particular piece that you are purchasing and why. If you are buying a current piece, certainly you should always try to get a box and sleeve. There would be few reasons to buy a current piece without them. When you are buying a piece on the Secondary Market, things are not as simple. Before deciding if you should buy a piece without a box or sleeve, take a few things into consideration. First, are you buying the piece for your own enjoyment or for investment. If for investment, by all means, try to get a piece with a box and sleeve. It will be much easier to sell on the secondary market and will command a higher price. If buying for enjoyment, however, don't let the fact that it doesn't have a box or sleeve make you pass on it. If it is a piece you really want and it is priced fairly, buy it. Remember you are buying a building or accessory - the box and sleeve are just that. I've never seen a display enhanced by the inclusion of a box or sleeve, have you?

There is no hard and fast rule as to how much less a piece without a box and sleeve should sell for on the Secondary Market. A starting place would be approximately 10% less than a piece of the same quality with a box and sleeve. Keep in mind that this is only a reference point and the percentage usually increases as the value of the piece decreases. Let me explain. If you had a piece worth $500, then the same piece would be worth roughly $450 without the box and sleeve. The buyer and seller could use that as a starting point to negotiate the final selling price. If you took 10% off a $100 piece however, a buyer would most likely opt to pass on the $90 price and spend the extra $10 to get one with a box and sleeve.

Q. *How can I keep up with all the news about my village?*

A. For an ongoing dialogue about our favorite hobby, subscribe to *the Village Chronicle. the Village Chronicle,* a speciality magazine for Department 56 collectors, is published and produced by my wife Jeanne and me. A bimonthly magazine, it offers page after page of news, information, articles, display tips, questions & answers, a calendar of D56 events and more. *the Village Chronicle* keeps you current with the latest trends and market values.

Learn things that you never knew about these great little houses ... refresh those that you did. Discover why collectors from all parts of the country consider *the Village Chronicle* to be a terrific source for information about Department 56. Collectors who love their villages never miss an issue, so subscribe today!

Call, mail or fax your subscription and be on your way to having even more fun with these fabulous houses that we all love so much!

$24 for one year (6 issues) *(Canada res: $29 US funds)*
$44 for two years (12 issues) *(Canada res: $49 US funds)*

Checks, Visa, MasterCard, Discover, American Express accepted

by mail:

the Village Chronicle
200 Post Rd Box 311
Warwick RI 02888-1535

by phone:

401-467-9343 (tel)
401-467-9359 (fax)

by internet:

d56er@aol.com
xxgk38a@prodigy.com

Happy Collecting!

THE HERITAGE VILLAGE COLLECTION

Accessories . . .

HVA84-1

CAROLERS
Group of village people sing or listen to carols.

HVA85-2

VILLAGE TRAIN
Three car porcelain train.

HVA86-3

CHRISTMAS CAROL FIGURES
Ebenezer Scrooge, Bob Cratchit carrying Tiny Tim, boy with poulterer/goose.

HVA86-4

LIGHTED TREE W/ CHILDREN AND LADDER
Children climb ladder to decorate tree.

HVA86-5

SLEIGHRIDE
Two horses draw old fashioned sleigh with a couple to enjoy ride.

HVA86-6

COVERED WOODEN BRIDGE
Simple wooden bridge with shingle roof to protect travelers from weather.

HVA86-7

NEW ENGLAND WINTER SET
Stone well, man pushes woman in swan sleigh, snow covered trees, man pulling tree.

HVA86-8

PORCELAIN TREES
Two different size snow covered evergreens.

ART CHART #	NAME	ITEM #	MATERIAL	SET?	!	MARKET STATUS	ORIGINAL SRP	GREENBOOK TRUMKT PRICE
	VARIATIONS/MISC/COLLECTOR NOTES							
HVA84-1	CAROLERS (1984) (DV)	6526-9	Porcelain	SET OF 3		RETIRED 1990	$ 10.00	$ 38.00
	There are three versions (sculpting/painting) of this set. Original "white post" @ $120.00. See footnote[1], page 250.							
HVA85-2	VILLAGE TRAIN (1985) (DV)	6527-7	Porcelain	SET OF 3		RETIRED 1986	12.00	475.00
	aka "Brighton Village Train."							
HVA86-3	CHRISTMAS CAROL FIGURES (1986) (DV)	6501-3	Porcelain	SET OF 3		RETIRED 1990	12.50	80.00
HVA86-4	LIGHTED TREE W/CHILDREN AND LADDER (1986) (CIC)	6510-2	Porcelain	NO	✓	RETIRED 1989	35.00	350.00
	Original sleeve reads, "Christmas In The City."							
HVA86-5	SLEIGHRIDE (1986) (DV, NE)	6511-0	Porcelain	NO		RETIRED 1990	19.50	50.00
	See footnote[2], page 250.							
HVA86-6	COVERED WOODEN BRIDGE (1986) (NE)	6531-5	Porcelain	NO		RETIRED 1990	10.00	35.00
	Variations: from light to dark.							
HVA86-7	NEW ENGLAND WINTER SET (1986) (NE)	6532-3	Porcelain	SET OF 5		RETIRED 1990	18.00	45.00
HVA86-8	PORCELAIN TREES (1986) (HV)	6537-4	Porcelain	SET OF 2		RETIRED 1992	14.00	35.00

HVA86-9

ALPINE VILLAGERS

Seated man, walking woman carrying book, dog pulling wagon with milk cans.

HVA87-10

FARM PEOPLE & ANIMALS

Man hauling logs. Woman and girl feeding geese. Goat pulls wagon and deer eat winter hay.

HVA87-11

BLACKSMITH

One man tends fire while smithy shoes horse and boy holds pail of nails.

HVA87-12

SILO & HAY SHED

Stone and stucco grain storage silo and elevated wood hay building.

HVA87-13

OX SLED

Heavy wood wagon on sled runners pulled by team of oxen. Driver plus small boy holding Christmas tree.

HVA87-14

CHRISTMAS IN THE CITY SIGN

Vertical emphasis on sign for Christmas In The City Collection.

HVA87-15

AUTOMOBILES

City delivery truck, checkered taxi, and roadster.

HVA87-16

CITY PEOPLE

Police officer, man walking dog, pretzel man with pushcart, mother and daughter with shopping bag, and woman collecting for the needy.

ART CHART #	NAME		ITEM #	MATERIAL	SET?	💡	MARKET STATUS	ORIGINAL SRP	GREENBOOK TRUMKT PRICE
	VARIATIONS/MISC/COLLECTOR NOTES								
HVA86-9	ALPINE VILLAGERS (1986)	(ALP)	6542-0	Porcelain	SET OF 3		RETIRED 1992	$ 13.00	$ 35.00
	Man and woman are thinner in later years of production.								
HVA87-10	FARM PEOPLE & ANIMALS (1987)	(DV)	5901-3	Porcelain	SET OF 5		RETIRED 1989	24.00	90.00
HVA87-11	BLACKSMITH (1987)	(DV)	5934-0	Porcelain	SET OF 3		RETIRED 1990	20.00	70.00
HVA87-12	SILO & HAY SHED (1987)	(DV)	5950-1	Porcelain	SET OF 2		RETIRED 1989	18.00	160.00
	1st issue: the roof of silo has stripes of rust, gold and brown; 2nd issue: silo has close to solid brown roof.								
HVA87-13	OX SLED (1987)	(DV)	5951-0	Porcelain	NO		RETIRED 1989	20.00	See Below*
	*Variations in color affect TRUMARKET Price: tan pants and green seat cushion @ $250, blue pants and black seat cushion @ $145.								
HVA87-14	CHRISTMAS IN THE CITY SIGN (1987)		5960-9	Porcelain	NO		RETIRED 1993	6.00	15.00
HVA87-15	AUTOMOBILES (1987)	(CIC)	5964-1	Porcelain	SET OF 3		CURRENT	15.00	22.00
HVA87-16	CITY PEOPLE (1987)	(CIC)	5965-0	Porcelain	SET OF 5		RETIRED 1990	27.50	50.00

HVA87-17 **SHOPKEEPERS** Vendors of fruits, vegetables, breads, cakes.	HVA87-18 **CITY WORKERS** Police constable, nurse, driver, tradesman with packages.	HVA87-19 **SKATING POND** Low stone wall circles pond. One child watches other child skating. Two snow covered trees.	HVA87-20 **STONE BRIDGE** Varigated fieldstone arches over river. Corner post has lamp.
HVA87-21 **VILLAGE WELL & HOLY CROSS** Old fashioned hand pump for water housed in small gazebo. & Cross upon pedestal on stone step base.	HVA87-22 Dickens' Village **DICKENS' VILLAGE SIGN**	HVA87-23 NEW ENGLAND VILLAGE **NEW ENGLAND VILLAGE SIGN**	HVA87-24 Alpine Village **ALPINE VILLAGE SIGN**

ART CHART #	NAME	ITEM #	MATERIAL	SET?		MARKET STATUS	ORIGINAL SRP	GREENBOOK TRUMKT PRICE
	VARIATIONS/MISC/COLLECTOR NOTES							
HVA87-17	SHOPKEEPERS (1987) (DV)	5966-8	Porcelain	SET OF 4		RETIRED 1988	$ 15.00	$ 38.00
	Along with the City Workers, the only figures to have "snow" sprinkled on them.							
HVA87-18	CITY WORKERS (1987) (DV)	5967-6	Porcelain	SET OF 4		RETIRED 1988	15.00	40.00
	Along with the Shopkeepers, the only figures to have "snow" sprinkled on them. Box reads "City People."							
HVA87-19	SKATING POND (1987) (DV, NE, CIC)	6545-5	Porcelain	NO		RETIRED 1990	24.00	75.00
	1st issue - made in Taiwan, ice is generally very light blue streaks; 2nd issue - made in Philippines, blue covers most of ice surface.							
HVA87-20	STONE BRIDGE (1987) (HV)	6546-3	Porcelain	NO		RETIRED 1990	12.00	80.00
	Variation in color from light to dark.							
HVA87-21	VILLAGE WELL & HOLY CROSS (1987) (DV)	6547-1	Porcelain	SET OF 2		RETIRED 1989	13.00	160.00
	1st issue - water is blue, birds are dark; 2nd issue - water has no color, birds are light.							
HVA87-22	DICKENS' VILLAGE SIGN (1987)	6569-2	Porcelain	NO		RETIRED 1993	6.00	20.00
HVA87-23	NEW ENGLAND VILLAGE SIGN (1987)	6570-6	Porcelain	NO		RETIRED 1993	6.00	15.00
HVA87-24	ALPINE VILLAGE SIGN (1987)	6571-4	Porcelain	NO		RETIRED 1993	6.00	20.00

HVA87-25

MAPLE SUGARING SHED
Two tapped trees, sled with bucket of syrup, & open walled shed w/cooking vat.

HVA87-26

DOVER COACH
Passenger coach with one horse, driver, and coachman.

HVA87-27

VILLAGE EXPRESS TRAIN
Black locomotive pulls a coal car, two passenger cars and a caboose.

HVA88-28

CHILDE POND AND SKATERS
Warming house, shutters latch against wind, wooden benches for skaters, brick building with birdhouse above door.

HVA88-29

FEZZIWIG AND FRIENDS
Husband and wife bringing food to elderly neighbors.

HVA88-30

NICHOLAS NICKLEBY CHARACTERS
Nicholas and sister Kate, Wackford Squeers with schoolbook, three children playing, and four-wheeled wagon.

HVA88-31

SNOW CHILDREN
Girl finishes snowman while dog watches. Two boys push off on sled, another bellyflops on his sled.

HVA88-32

VILLAGE HARVEST PEOPLE
Woman with butter churn, man loads pumpkins on cart, corn shocks, and pumpkins.

ART CHART #	NAME		ITEM #	MATERIAL	SET?	!	MARKET STATUS	ORIGINAL SRP	GREENBOOK TRUMKT PRICE
	VARIATIONS/MISC/COLLECTOR NOTES								
HVA87-25	MAPLE SUGARING SHED (1987)	(NE)	6589-7	Porcelain	SET OF 3		RETIRED 1989	$ 19.00	$ 245.00
HVA87-26	DOVER COACH (1987)	(DV)	6590-0	Porcelain	NO		RETIRED 1990	18.00	See Below*
	*Variations affect TRUMARKET Price, see footnote[3], page 250.								
HVA87-27	VILLAGE EXPRESS TRAIN - BLACK (1987)	(HV)	5997-8	------	SET OF 22		RETIRED 1988	90.00	300.00
	Manufactured by Tyco.								
HVA88-28	CHILDE POND AND SKATERS (1988)	(DV)	5903-0	Porcelain	SET OF 4		RETIRED 1991	30.00	80.00
	Variation: color of warming hut varies.								
HVA88-29	FEZZIWIG AND FRIENDS (1988)	(DV)	5928-5	Porcelain	SET OF 3		RETIRED 1990	12.50	50.00
	Addition to "Christmas Carol" grouping.								
HVA88-30	NICHOLAS NICKLEBY CHARACTERS (1988)	(DV)	5929-3	Porcelain	SET OF 4		RETIRED 1991	20.00	36.00
	Misspelled as Nicholas Nick"el"by on sleeve.								
HVA88-31	SNOW CHILDREN (1988)	(HV)	5938-2	Porcelain	SET OF 3		RETIRED 1994	15.00	22.00
HVA88-32	VILLAGE HARVEST PEOPLE (1988)	(NE)	5941-2	Porcelain	SET OF 4		RETIRED 1991	27.50	45.00
	Sleeve reads "Harvest Time."								

HVA88-33

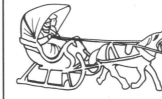

CITY NEWSSTAND
News vendor, magazine and newspaper wooden stand, woman reading paper, newsboy showing headlines.

HVA88-34

VILLAGE TRAIN TRESTLE
Double arch trestle spans river. One track on stone train bridge.

HVA88-35

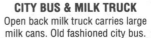

ONE HORSE OPEN SLEIGH
Couple out for a ride in sleigh with canopy. Lap robes protect against cold.

HVA88-36

CITY BUS & MILK TRUCK
Open back milk truck carries large milk cans. Old fashioned city bus.

HVA88-37

SALVATION ARMY BAND
Five instrumentalists and conductor in uniform of charitable organization.

HVA88-38

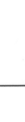

WOODCUTTER AND SON
Father splits logs and son carries cordwood.

HVA88-39

RED COVERED BRIDGE
Wooden bridge spans Maple Creek supported by stone bases.

HVA88-40

VILLAGE EXPRESS TRAIN
Red, black and silver locomotive pulls the cars around the track.

ART CHART #	NAME		ITEM #	MATERIAL	SET?	!	MARKET STATUS	ORIGINAL SRP	GREENBOOK TRUMKT PRICE
	VARIATIONS/MISC/COLLECTOR NOTES								
HVA88-33	CITY NEWSSTAND (1988)	(CIC)	5971-4	Porcelain	SET OF 4		RETIRED 1991	$ 25.00	$ 48.00
HVA88-34	VILLAGE TRAIN TRESTLE (1988)	(HV)	5981-1	Porcelain	NO		RETIRED 1990	17.00	60.00
	Sleeve reads "Stone Train Trestle."								
HVA88-35	ONE HORSE OPEN SLEIGH (1988)	(HV)	5982-0	Porcelain	NO		RETIRED 1993	20.00	35.00
HVA88-36	CITY BUS & MILK TRUCK (1988)	(CIC)	5983-8	Porcelain	SET OF 2		RETIRED 1991	15.00	32.00
	Box reads "Transport."								
HVA88-37	SALVATION ARMY BAND (1988)	(CIC)	5985-4	Porcelain	SET OF 6		RETIRED 1991	24.00	65.00
HVA88-38	WOODCUTTER AND SON (1988)	(NE)	5986-2	Porcelain	SET OF 2		RETIRED 1990	10.00	40.00
HVA88-39	RED COVERED BRIDGE (1988)	(NE)	5987-0	Porcelain	NO		RETIRED 1994	15.00	22.00
HVA88-40	VILLAGE EXPRESS TRAIN - RED, SILVER (1988)	(HV)	5980-3	------	SET OF 22		CURRENT	95.00	100.00
	Manufactured by Bachmann Trains.								

HVA89-41

DAVID COPPERFIELD CHARACTERS

David Copperfield, Agnes, Mr. Wickfield, Peggotty with young David and Emily, Betsy Trotwood with Mr. Dick.

HVA89-42

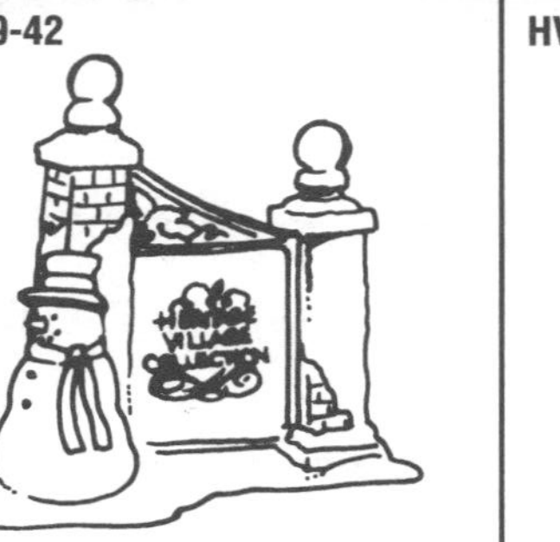

VILLAGE SIGN WITH SNOWMAN

Snowman with top hat and scarf next to brick pillars and Heritage Village Sign.

HVA89-43

LAMPLIGHTER W/LAMP

Man carries lit torch to light street lamps for evening. Old fashioned lam post, small tree by post.

HVA89-44

ROYAL COACH

Royal Coat Of Arms on door of gold filigree decorated red coach, wheel base and undercarriage of cast metal, four gray horses with red and gold trim.

HVA89-45

CONSTABLES

One holds club, one with seated dog, one tips hat and stands by lamppost.

HVA89-46

VIOLET VENDOR/CAROLERS/ CHESTNUT VENDOR

Elderly woman sells violet bunches from basket, man sells fresh roasted nuts, and two women singing carols.

HVA89-47

KINGS ROAD CAB

Two wheeled horse drawn carriage. Driver sits high and behind cab. Passengers protected from weather.

HVA89-48

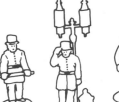

CHRISTMAS MORNING FIGURES

Scrooge transformed - smiling, small boy by fence and lamppost - waving, couple carrying presents.

ART CHART #	NAME	ITEM #	MATERIAL	SET?	!	MARKET STATUS	ORIGINAL SRP	GREENBOOK TRUMKT PRICE
	VARIATIONS/MISC/COLLECTOR NOTES							
HVA89-41	DAVID COPPERFIELD CHARACTERS (1989) (DV)	5551-4	Porcelain	SET OF 5		RETIRED 1992	$ 32.50	$ 48.00
HVA89-42	VILLAGE SIGN WITH SNOWMAN (1989) (HV)	5572-7	Porcelain	NO		RETIRED 1994	10.00	12.00
	Size is 3".							
HVA89-43	LAMPLIGHTER W/LAMP (1989) (DV)	5577-8	Porcelain	SET OF 2		CURRENT	9.00	10.00
HVA89-44	ROYAL COACH (1989) (DV)	5578-6	Prcln/Metal	NO		RETIRED 1992	55.00	75.00
	Early release to National Association Of Limited Edition Dealers.							
HVA89-45	CONSTABLES (1989) (DV)	5579-4	Porcelain	SET OF 3		RETIRED 1991	17.50	60.00
HVA89-46	VIOLET VENDOR/CAROLERS/CHESTNUT VENDOR (1989) (DV)	5580-8	Porcelain	SET OF 3		RETIRED 1992	23.00	40.00
HVA89-47	KINGS ROAD CAB (1989) (DV)	5581-6	Porcelain	NO		CURRENT	30.00	30.00
HVA89-48	CHRISTMAS MORNING FIGURES (1989) (DV)	5588-3	Porcelain	SET OF 3		CURRENT	18.00	18.00
	Early release to National Association Of Limited Edition Dealers. Addition to "Christmas Carol" grouping.							

HVA89-49

CHRISTMAS SPIRITS FIGURES

Scrooge with Ghost Of ...
1) Christmas Past, 2) Christmas Present, and 3) Future...&...Marley.

HVA89-50

FARM ANIMALS

Chickens, geese, sheep, ewe and lamb.

HVA89-51

ORGAN GRINDER

Man turns handle to produce music for little monkey to dance. Woman and girl watch monkey.

HVA89-52

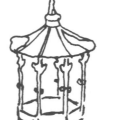

POPCORN VENDOR

Truck with red and white striped top. Vendor fills red and white bag. Little girl has a full popcorn bag.

HVA89-53

RIVER STREET ICE HOUSE CART

Horse pulls a blue and gray ice wagon for iceman.

HVA89-54

CENTRAL PARK CARRIAGE

Gray horse pulls red and black carrriage. Driver has mother and child as passengers.

HVA89-55

TOWN SQUARE GAZEBO

Eight posts support the roof that rises to a spire. Stone work on floor follows the shape of the roof.

HVA89-56

BOULEVARD

Forms a tree-lined sidewalk. Trees provide shade at benches.

ART CHART #	NAME		ITEM #	MATERIAL	SET?	💡	MARKET STATUS	ORIGINAL SRP	GREENBOOK TRUMKT PRICE
	VARIATIONS/MISC/COLLECTOR NOTES								
HVA89-49	CHRISTMAS SPIRITS FIGURES (1989)	(DV)	5589-1	Porcelain	SET OF 4		CURRENT	$ 27.50	$ 27.50
	Addition to "Christmas Carol" grouping.								
HVA89-50	FARM ANIMALS (1989)	(NE)	5945-5	Porcelain	SET OF 4		RETIRED 1991	15.00	40.00
HVA89-51	ORGAN GRINDER (1989)	(CIC)	5957-9	Porcelain	SET OF 3		RETIRED 1991	21.00	35.00
HVA89-52	POPCORN VENDOR (1989)	(CIC)	5958-7	Porcelain	SET OF 3		RETIRED 1992	22.00	40.00
HVA89-53	RIVER STREET ICE HOUSE CART (1989)	(CIC)	5959-5	Porcelain	NO		RETIRED 1991	20.00	50.00
HVA89-54	CENTRAL PARK CARRIAGE (1989)	(CIC)	5979-0	Porcelain	NO		CURRENT	30.00	30.00
HVA89-55	TOWN SQUARE GAZEBO (1989)	(HV)	5513-1	Resin	NO		CURRENT	19.00	19.00
HVA89-56	BOULEVARD (1989)	(CIC)	5516-6	------	SET OF 14		RETIRED 1992	25.00	50.00
	4 sidewalk pieces, 4 removable 5" trees, 2 benches, 4 hitching posts.								

HVA89-57

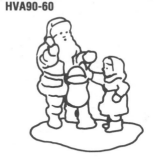

MAILBOX & FIRE HYDRANT
Red, white and blue mail box features "U.S. Mail" sign and eagle logo.

HVA89-58

HV PROMOTIONAL SIGN
Vertical sign with arched top and brick base. Gold lettering on white facade.

HVA90-59

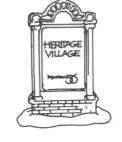

BUSY SIDEWALKS
Delivery boy, doorman, two elderly ladies, mother with toddler and baby in carriage.

HVA90-60

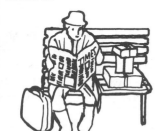

'TIS THE SEASON
Santa with bell and iron kettle for Season donations. Little girl gives to the needy.

HVA90-61

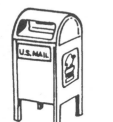

REST YE MERRY GENTLEMAN
Man sits on bench reading newspaper with purchases all around him.

HVA90-62

TOWN CRIER & CHIMNEY SWEEP
Crier rings bell and reads out announcements. A Sweep in top hat and tails carries chimney brush.

HVA90-63

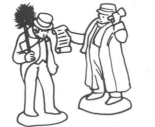

CAROLERS ON THE DOORSTEP
Four children sing carols to elderly man and woman - boys carry lanterns, girls have songbooks.

HVA90-64

HOLIDAY TRAVELERS
Train conductor, baggage handler, and man and woman passengers.

ART CHART #	NAME		ITEM #	MATERIAL	SET?	!	MARKET STATUS	ORIGINAL SRP	GREENBOOK TRUMKT PRICE
	VARIATIONS/MISC/COLLECTOR NOTES								
HVA89-57	MAILBOX & FIRE HYDRANT (1989)	(CIC)	5517-4	Metal	NO		RETIRED 1990	$ 6.00	$ 20.00
	US Post Office - Red, White & Blue.								
HVA89-58	HV PROMOTIONAL SIGN (1989)	(HV)	9953-8	Earthenware	NO		RETIRED 1990	5.00	20.00
	Variation: green lettering on green facade.								
HVA90-59	BUSY SIDEWALKS (1990)	(CIC)	5535-2	Porcelain	SET OF 4		RETIRED 1992	28.00	45.00
HVA90-60	'TIS THE SEASON (1990)	(CIC)	5539-5	Porcelain	NO		RETIRED 1994	12.50	20.00
HVA90-61	REST YE MERRY GENTLEMAN (1990)	(CIC)	5540-9	Prcln/Metal	NO		CURRENT	12.50	12.95
HVA90-62	TOWN CRIER & CHIMNEY SWEEP (1990)	(DV)	5569-7	Porcelain	SET OF 2		CURRENT	15.00	16.00
HVA90-63	CAROLERS ON THE DOORSTEP (1990)	(DV)	5570-0	Porcelain	SET OF 4		RETIRED 1993	25.00	40.00
HVA90-64	HOLIDAY TRAVELERS (1990)	(DV)	5571-9	Porcelain	SET OF 3		CURRENT	22.50	25.00

HVA90-65

THE FLYING SCOT TRAIN

Engine and wood supply car and two passenger cars with luggage carriers atop cars.

HVA90-66

VICTORIA STATION TRAIN PLATFORM

Ticket booth with windows all around, long metal roof to protect passengers.

HVA90-67

TRIMMING THE NORTH POLE

One elf holds another to put greenery on North Pole sign while blue bird watches.

HVA90-68

SANTA & MRS. CLAUS

Mrs. Claus with elf waves good-bye. Santa checks book before leaving N. Pole.

HVA90-69

SANTA'S LITTLE HELPERS

Elf stands on presents to hang wreath. Two elves move toy sack. One elf brings two reindeer to sleigh.

HVA90-70

SLEIGH & EIGHT TINY REINDEER

Toys fill sleigh harnessed to Santa's eight reindeer.

HVA90-71

THE TOY PEDDLER

Toyman carries tray with toys. Mother and son look at toy horse. Little girl holds top.

HVA90-72

AMISH FAMILY

Mother carries apples in apron, father stacks apple boxes, children sort apples.

ART CHART #	NAME		ITEM #	MATERIAL	SET?	!	MARKET STATUS	ORIGINAL SRP	GREENBOOK TRUMKT PRICE
	VARIATIONS/MISC/COLLECTOR NOTES								
HVA90-65	THE FLYING SCOT TRAIN (1990)	(DV)	5573-5	Porcelain	SET OF 4		CURRENT	$ 48.00	$ 50.00
HVA90-66	VICTORIA STATION TRAIN PLATFORM (1990)	(DV)	5575-1	Prcln/Metal	NO		CURRENT	20.00	22.00
HVA90-67	TRIMMING THE NORTH POLE (1990)	(NP)	5608-1	Porcelain	NO		RETIRED 1993	10.00	22.00
HVA90-68	SANTA & MRS. CLAUS (1990)	(NP)	5609-0	Porcelain	SET OF 2		CURRENT	15.00	15.00
	Variation exists in title on book: "Good Boys" instead of "Good Kids."								
HVA90-69	SANTA'S LITTLE HELPERS (1990)	(NP)	5610-3	Porcelain	SET OF 3		RETIRED 1993	28.00	48.00
HVA90-70	SLEIGH & EIGHT TINY REINDEER (1990)	(NP)	5611-1	Porcelain	SET OF 5		CURRENT	40.00	42.00
HVA90-71	THE TOY PEDDLER (1990)	(ALP)	5616-2	Porcelain	SET OF 3		CURRENT	22.00	22.00
HVA90-72	AMISH FAMILY (1990)	(NE)	5948-0	Porcelain	SET OF 3		RETIRED 1992	20.00	35.00
	Early release to Showcase Dealers and the National Association Of Limited Edition Dealers. Variation: with mustache @ $50.								

HVA90-73

AMISH BUGGY

Amish man feeds brown horse harnessed to family privacy curtained carriage.

HVA90-74

SLEEPY HOLLOW CHARACTERS

Man carving pumpkin, Squire and Mrs. VanTassel, Ichabod Crane with children.

HVA90-75

MAILBOX & FIRE HYDRANT

Red & green mail box & red fire hydrant.

HVA91-76

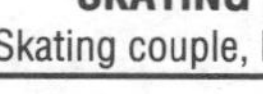

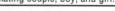

SKATING PARTY

Skating couple, boy, and girl.

HVA91-77

ALL AROUND THE TOWN

Man with "sandwich boards" as a walking ad for "White Christmas." Man with packages stops to get his shoes shined from young boy.

HVA91-78

THE FIRE BRIGADE

Two firemen carry ladder and ax. Fireman with pail takes moment to pet mascot dalmatian.

HVA91-79

"CITY FIRE DEPT" FIRE TRUCK

Ladder attached to side, hose and nozzle assembly on top and rear of red fire truck.

HVA91-80

CAROLING THRU THE CITY

Singing man pulls sled with two boys, two women with young girl, man (alone) all with song books.

ART CHART #	NAME		ITEM #	MATERIAL	SET?	!	MARKET STATUS	ORIGINAL SRP	GREENBOOK TRUMKT PRICE
	VARIATIONS/MISC/COLLECTOR NOTES								
HVA90-73	AMISH BUGGY (1990)	(NE)	5949-8	Porcelain	NO		RETIRED 1992	$ 22.00	$ 50.00
HVA90-74	SLEEPY HOLLOW CHARACTERS (1990)	(NE)	5956-0	Porcelain	SET OF 3		RETIRED 1992	27.50	45.00
HVA90-75	MAILBOX & FIRE HYDRANT (1990)	(CIC)	5214-0	Metal	SET OF 2		CURRENT	5.00	5.00
	Green & Red HV Mail Box. Replaced #5517-4, (HVA89-57).								
HVA91-76	SKATING PARTY (1991)	(NE)	5523-9	Porcelain	SET OF 3		CURRENT	27.50	27.50
HVA91-77	ALL AROUND THE TOWN (1991)	(CIC)	5545-0	Porcelain	SET OF 2		RETIRED 1993	18.00	30.00
HVA91-78	THE FIRE BRIGADE (1991)	(CIC)	5546-8	Porcelain	SET OF 2		CURRENT	20.00	20.00
HVA91-79	"CITY FIRE DEPT." FIRE TRUCK (1991)	(CIC)	5547-6	Porcelain	NO		CURRENT	18.00	18.00
HVA91-80	CAROLING THRU THE CITY (1991)	(CIC)	5548-4	Porcelain	SET OF 3		CURRENT	27.50	27.50

HVA91-81

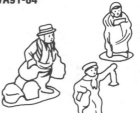

OLIVER TWIST CHARACTERS

Mr. Brownlow in long coat, stovepipe hat, walks with cane. Oliver in rags next to food cart as another boy reaches to steal food, third boy holds sack.

HVA91-82

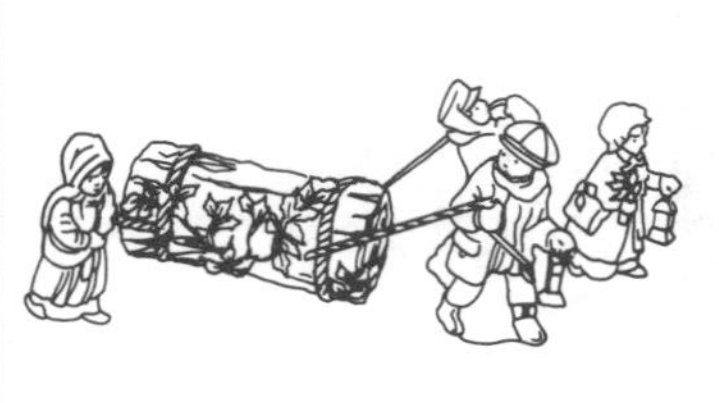

BRINGING HOME THE YULE LOG

Two boys pull on ropes to haul log. One girl holds lantern to light way and another walks alongside.

HVA91-83

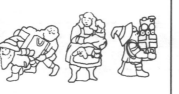

POULTRY MARKET

Aproned poulterer holds game bird. Covered stand with display of turkeys and geese. Woman holds purchase as child watches.

HVA91-84

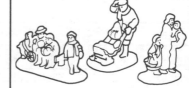

COME INTO THE INN

Innkeeper's wife reads note between sweeping snow from entry. Young boy with lantern lights way for coach driver. Gentleman carries luggage to the inn.

HVA91-85

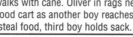

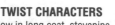

HOLIDAY COACH

Four horses pull coach full of travelers who ride inside and on topside seats. Coachman blows horn on arrival as driver guides horses.

HVA91-86

TOYMAKER ELVES

Two elves carry trunk of toys. One elf balances stack of toys. One elf has apron filled with toys.

HVA91-87

BAKER ELVES

One elf holds piece of belled harness from sleigh. One elf holds tray of baked goods. One elf takes a cookie from Sweets Cart.

HVA91-88

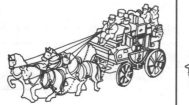

MARKET DAY

Mother carrying baby and basket and daughter with basket of bread. Aproned merchant tips hat as he pushes sledge with bagged food. Man and boy rest on goat pulled cart while standing boy holds bag.

ART CHART #	NAME	ITEM #	MATERIAL	SET?	!	MARKET STATUS	ORIGINAL SRP	GREENBOOK TRUMKT PRICE
	VARIATIONS/MISC/COLLECTOR NOTES							
HVA91-81	OLIVER TWIST CHARACTERS (1991) (DV)	5554-9	Porcelain	SET OF 3		RETIRED 1993	$ 35.00	$ 45.00
HVA91-82	BRINGING HOME THE YULE LOG (1991) (DV)	5558-1	Porcelain	SET OF 3		CURRENT	27.50	28.00
HVA91-83	POULTRY MARKET (1991) (DV)	5559-0	Porcelain	SET OF 3		CURRENT	30.00	32.00
	Variation: original "proof" version with patches on drape.							
HVA91-84	COME INTO THE INN (1991) (DV)	5560-3	Porcelain	SET OF 3		RETIRED 1994	22.00	26.00
HVA91-85	HOLIDAY COACH (1991) (DV)	5561-1	Porcelain	NO		CURRENT	68.00	70.00
	Variation: gold chains vs. silver chains.							
HVA91-86	TOYMAKER ELVES (1991) (NP)	5602-2	Porcelain	SET OF 3		CURRENT	27.50	27.50
HVA91-87	BAKER ELVES (1991) (NP)	5603-0	Porcelain	SET OF 3		CURRENT	27.50	27.50
HVA91-88	MARKET DAY (1991) (NE)	5641-3	Porcelain	SET OF 3		RETIRED 1993	35.00	45.00

HVA92-89

GATE HOUSE

Originated as tower over fortified entrance of a castle's perimeter wall. Brick base with arched entry made for passage of carriages/wagons. Windows narrow and shuttered to close against weather and attack.

HVA92-90

CHURCHYARD FENCE & GATE

Stone base with wrought iron atop, acted as barrier to protect land around church which usually included graveyard. One curved section, one straight section, one section with iron gate set in stone arch.

HVA92-91

DON'T DROP THE PRESENTS!

Mother cautions father to take care as dog jumps up to sniff presents in father's arms. Daughter peeks out from mother's skirt as full shopping bag rests on snow. Son slips and tumbles in snow.

HVA92-92

WELCOME HOME

Boy reaches to hug Grandmother visiting for holiday as girl and Grandfather reach out to hug each other. Family pet joins the greeting.

HVA92-93

LETTERS FOR SANTA

One elf carries bundles of letters, as another elf tries to lift sack of letters. Two additional elves arrive with reindeer cart filled with mail bags of letters for Santa.

HVA92-94

TESTING THE TOYS

One elf rides downhill on a sled as two others try out a toboggan.

HVA92-95

BUYING BAKER'S BREAD

Man and woman lift basket together to carry loaves, plus she carries basket on arm. Man carries basket tray of bread while rest of loaves are carried in his basket backpack.

HVA92-96

HARVEST SEED CART

Boy lifts sack of corn to place on barrow. Man lifts barrow filled with corn sacks as one chicken pecks at sack and one chicken walks next to him. Girl holds white rooster and has basket resting on ground by her feet.

ART CHART #	NAME	ITEM #	MATERIAL	SET?	!	MARKET STATUS	ORIGINAL SRP	GREENBOOK TRUMKT PRICE
	VARIATIONS/MISC/COLLECTOR NOTES							
HVA92-89	GATE HOUSE (1992) (HV)	5530-1	Porcelain	NO		SEE BELOW*	$ 22.50	$ 55.00
	*Available at 1992 Village Gatherings and select Showcase Dealer Open Houses. Variations in color of stone brick between shades of gray or blue.							
HVA92-90	CHURCHYARD FENCE & GATE (1992) (DV, NE, CIC)	5563-8	Porcelain	SET OF 3		DISCONTINUED*	15.00	40.00
	Early release to Gift Creations Concepts. *See footnote[4], page 250.							
HVA92-91	DON'T DROP THE PRESENTS! (1992) (CIC)	5532-8	Porcelain	SET OF 2		CURRENT	25.00	25.00
HVA92-92	WELCOME HOME (1992) (CIC)	5533-6	Porcelain	SET OF 3		CURRENT	27.50	27.50
HVA92-93	LETTERS FOR SANTA (1992) (NP)	5604-9	Porcelain	SET OF 3		RETIRED 1994	30.00	50.00
HVA92-94	TESTING THE TOYS (1992) (NP)	5605-7	Porcelain	SET OF 2		CURRENT	16.50	16.50
HVA92-95	BUYING BAKERS BREAD (1992) (ALP)	5619-7	Porcelain	SET OF 2		CURRENT	20.00	20.00
HVA92-96	HARVEST SEED CART (1992) (DV, NE)	5645-6	Porcelain	SET OF 3		CURRENT	27.50	27.50

HVA92-97

TOWN TINKER

Traveling salesman with covered cart he lifts and push/pulls. He sold pots, pans, trinkets, and all manner of odds and ends. He made repairs as well, going from house to house, village to village.

HVA92-98

THE OLD PUPPETEER

Children watch puppet show. Stage on wheels with man moving the stringed marionettes to tell stories to audiences of all ages.

HVA92-99

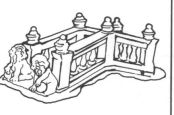

THE BIRD SELLER

Woman holds up two bird cages. Delighted child and mother with woman who has made her purchase.

HVA92-100

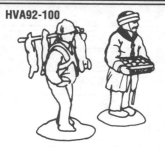

VILLAGE STREET PEDDLERS

One man carries pole of fresh dressed rabbits. Second peddler wears wooden tray of spices to be sold in small pinches and ounces.

HVA92-101

CHURCHYARD GATE AND FENCE

Arched gate of stone and wrought iron connects to low stone fence topped by low wrought iron posts and connectors.

HVA92-102

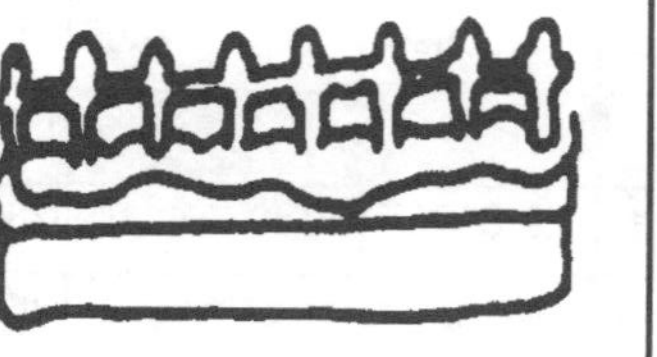

CHURCHYARD FENCE EXTENSIONS

Stone base with wrought iron posts and connectors to extend fence around church and graveyard.

HVA92-103

LIONHEAD BRIDGE

Massive bridge with two stone lions, each with one raised paw resting on a sphere.

HVA92-104

VILLAGE EXPRESS VAN

Green delivery van advertises On Time Service. Rack on van roof holds wrapped packages.

ART CHART #	NAME		ITEM #	MATERIAL	SET?	!	MARKET STATUS	ORIGINAL SRP	GREENBOOK TRUMKT PRICE
	VARIATIONS/MISC/COLLECTOR NOTES								
HVA92-97	TOWN TINKER (1992)	(DV, NE)	5646-4	Porcelain	SET OF 2		CURRENT	$ 24.00	$ 24.00
HVA92-98	THE OLD PUPPETEER (1992)	(DV)	5802-5	Porcelain	SET OF 3		CURRENT	32.00	32.00
HVA92-99	THE BIRD SELLER (1992)	(DV)	5803-3	Porcelain	SET OF 3		CURRENT	25.00	25.00
HVA92-100	VILLAGE STREET PEDDLERS (1992)	(DV)	5804-1	Porcelain	SET OF 2		RETIRED 1994	16.00	22.00
HVA92-101	CHURCHYARD GATE AND FENCE (1992)	(HV)	5806-8	Porcelain	SET OF 3		CURRENT	15.00	15.00
	See footnote[4], page 250.								
HVA92-102	CHURCHYARD FENCE EXTENSIONS (1992)	(HV)	5807-6	Porcelain	SET OF 4		CURRENT	16.00	16.00
	See footnote[4], page 250.								
HVA92-103	LIONHEAD BRIDGE (1992)	(DV)	5864-5	Porcelain	NO		CURRENT	22.00	22.00
HVA92-104	VILLAGE EXPRESS VAN (1992)	(CIC)	5865-3	Porcelain	NO		CURRENT	25.00	25.00
	Color is green. Size is 4.5" x 3". License plate is abbreviated address of D56 headquarters, 6436 City West Parkway.								

HVA92-105

VILLAGE EXPRESS VAN
Special black delivery van advertises On Time Service. Rack on van roof holds wrapped packages.

HVA92-106

ENGLISH POST BOX
Red six-sided, English-styled post box.

HVA93-107

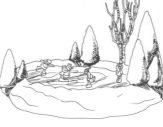

VILLAGE ANIMATED SKATING POND
Skaters move alone or as pair in set patterns on ice pond surface.

HVA93-108

PLAYING IN THE SNOW
Children build and dress a snowman.

HVA93-109

STREET MUSICIANS
Girl gives coin to the street musicians.

HVA93-110

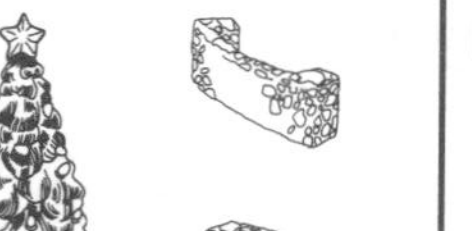

TOWN TREE
Decorated town tree and stone sections to encircle tree.

HVA93-111

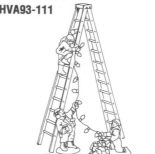

TOWN TREE TRIMMERS
Ladder and three helpers to decorate town tree.

HVA93-112

CLIMB EVERY MOUNTAIN
Three climbers and companion St. Bernard dog roped together for safety.

ART CHART #	NAME		ITEM #	MATERIAL	SET?	💡	MARKET STATUS	ORIGINAL SRP	GREENBOOK TRUMKT PRICE
	VARIATIONS/MISC/COLLECTOR NOTES								
HVA92-105	VILLAGE EXPRESS VAN - BLACK (1992)	(CIC)	9951-1	Porcelain	NO		PROMOTIONAL*	$ 25.00	$ 125.00
	Special black van. Size is 4.5" x 3". *Bachman's Gathering & given to sales representatives as a gift at National Sales Conference, 12/92								
HVA92-106	ENGLISH POST BOX (1992)	(DV)	5805-0	Metal	NO		CURRENT	4.50	4.50
HVA93-107	VILLAGE ANIMATED SKATING POND (1993)	(HV)	5229-9	--------	SET OF 15		CURRENT	60.00	60.00
	Electrical								
HVA93-108	PLAYING IN THE SNOW (1993)	(CIC)	5556-5	Porcelain	SET OF 3		CURRENT	25.00	25.00
HVA93-109	STREET MUSICIANS (1993)	(CIC)	5564-6	Porcelain	SET OF 3		CURRENT	25.00	25.00
HVA93-110	TOWN TREE (1993)	(CIC)	5565-4	Porcelain	SET OF 5	✓	CURRENT	45.00	45.00
HVA93-111	TOWN TREE TRIMMERS(1993)	(CIC)	5566-2	Porcelain	SET OF 4		CURRENT	32.50	32.50
HVA93-112	CLIMB EVERY MOUNTAIN (1993)	(ALP)	5613-8	Porcelain	SET OF 4		CURRENT	27.50	27.50

HVA93-113

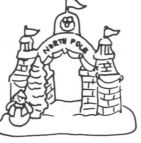

WOODSMEN ELVES
Elves cut tree and wood to warm North Pole buildings.

HVA93-114

SING A SONG FOR SANTA
Caroling North Pole elves.

HVA93-115

NORTH POLE GATE
Entry gate to North Pole Village.

HVA93-116

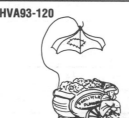

KNIFE GRINDER
Man powered grinding wheel keeps sharp edge for knives and tools.

HVA93-117

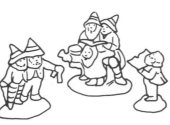

BLUE STAR ICE HARVESTERS
Men cut up pond, lake, and river ice for use in icehouse for food storage and cooling.

HVA93-118

CHELSEA MARKET FRUIT MONGER & CART
Pushcart vendor of fresh fruits and vegetables.

HVA93-119

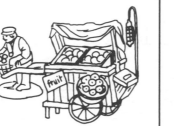

CHELSEA MARKET FISH MONGER & CART
Pushcart vendor of fresh fish.

HVA93-120

CHELSEA MARKET FLOWER MONGER & CART
Pushcart vendor of fresh cut flowers and nosegays.

ART CHART #	NAME		ITEM #	MATERIAL	SET?	!	MARKET STATUS	ORIGINAL SRP	GREENBOOK TRUMKT PRICE
	VARIATIONS/MISC/COLLECTOR NOTES								
HVA93-113	WOODSMEN ELVES (1993)	(NP)	5630-8	Porcelain	SET OF 3		CURRENT	$ 30.00	$ 30.00
HVA93-114	SING A SONG FOR SANTA (1993)	(NP)	5631-6	Porcelain	SET OF 3		CURRENT	28.00	28.00
HVA93-115	NORTH POLE GATE (1993)	(NP)	5632-4	Porcelain	NO		CURRENT	32.50	32.50
HVA93-116	KNIFE GRINDER (1993)	(NE)	5649-9	Porcelain	SET OF 2		CURRENT	22.50	22.50
HVA93-117	BLUE STAR ICE HARVESTERS (1993)	(NE)	5650-2	Porcelain	SET OF 2		CURRENT	27.50	27.50
HVA93-118	CHELSEA MARKET FRUIT MONGER & CART (1993)	(DV)	5813-0	Porcelain	SET OF 2		CURRENT	25.00	25.00
HVA93-119	CHELSEA MARKET FISH MONGER & CART (1993)	(DV)	5814-9	Porcelain	SET OF 2		CURRENT	25.00	25.00
HVA93-120	CHELSEA MARKET FLOWER MONGER & CART (1993)	(DV)	5815-7	Porcelain	SET OF 2		CURRENT	27.50	27.50

HVA93-121

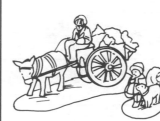

CHELSEA LANE SHOPPERS
Woman and girl, each with flowers.
Couple walking with package and basket.
Gentleman with walking stick.

HVA93-122

VISION OF A CHRISTMAS PAST
Innkeeper with coach dogs,
traveling merchant, 2 young travelers.

HVA93-123

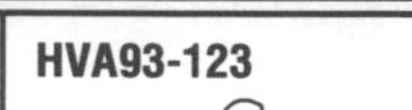

C. BRADFORD, WHEELWRIGHT & SON
Father and son wagon wheel
makers and repairers.

HVA93-124

BRINGING FLEECES TO THE MILL
Shepherd takes wagonload of fleeces
to market. Child stands with sheep.

HVA93-125

DASHING THROUGH THE SNOW
Horse drawn sleigh takes couple
for ride across snowy roads.

HVA93-126

CHRISTMAS AT THE PARK
Seated father, mother and child.
Seated boy and girl with dog.

HVA93-127

VILLAGE EXPRESS VAN
Gold "Road Show" Edition.
Rack on van holds wrapped packages

HVA94-128

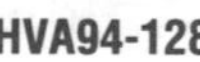

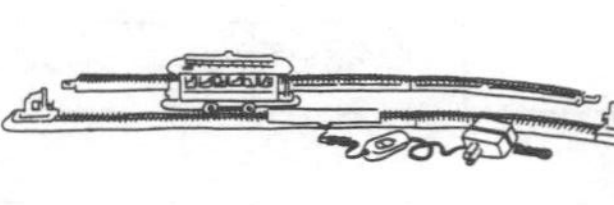

VILLAGE STREETCAR
Track setup for inner city traveling.
Car lights up.
Passengers visible thru windows.

ART CHART #	NAME	ITEM #	MATERIAL	SET?	!	MARKET STATUS	ORIGINAL SRP	GREENBOOK TRUMKT PRICE
	VARIATIONS/MISC/COLLECTOR NOTES							
HVA93-121	CHELSEA LANE SHOPPERS (1993) (DV)	5816-5	Porcelain	SET OF 4		CURRENT	$ 30.00	$ 30.00
HVA93-122	VISION OF A CHRISTMAS PAST (1993) (DV)	5817-3	Porcelain	SET OF 3		CURRENT	27.50	27.50
HVA93-123	C. BRADFORD, WHEELWRIGHT & SON (1993) (DV)	5818-1	Porcelain	SET OF 2		CURRENT	24.00	24.00
HVA93-124	BRINGING FLEECES TO THE MILL (1993) (DV)	5819-0	Porcelain	SET OF 2		CURRENT	35.00	35.00
HVA93-125	DASHING THROUGH THE SNOW (1993) (DV)	5820-3	Porcelain	NO		CURRENT	32.50	32.50
HVA93-126	CHRISTMAS AT THE PARK (1993) (CIC)	5866-1	Porcelain	SET OF 3		CURRENT	27.50	27.50
HVA93-127	VILLAGE EXPRESS VAN - GOLD (1993) (CIC)	9977-5	Porcelain	NO		PROMOTIONAL*	25.00	1200.00
	"Road Show" Edition. Packed in gold box. *Presented to potential investors before initial public offering.							
HVA94-128	VILLAGE STREETCAR (1994) (CIC)	5240-0	---------	SET OF 10		CURRENT	65.00	65.00
	Manufactured by Bachmann Trains.							

HVA94-129

POSTERN

Arched, timbered entryway connected to gatehouse.
Flag fliews from atop the arch; village sign hangs below it.

HVA94-130

VILLAGE EXPRESS VAN FOR GATHERINGS

Black van for store delivery service.
Right side is D56 logo and left side is ad for specific D56 dealer.

ART CHART #	NAME	ITEM #	MATERIAL	SET?	!	MARKET STATUS	ORIGINAL SRP	GREENBOOK TRUMKT PRICE
	VARIATIONS/MISC/COLLECTOR NOTES							
HVA94-129	POSTERN (1994) (DV)	9871-0	Porcelain	NO		1994 ANNUAL	$ 17.50	$ 25.00
	Dickens' Village Ten Year Anniversary Piece. Cornerstone with dates. Special commemorative imprint on bottom.							
HVA94-130	VILLAGE EXPRESS VAN - PROMOTIONAL (1994) (CIC)	See Below	Porcelain	NO		PROMOTIONAL	25.00	See Below

14 black Village Express Vans were produced for 1994 dealer promotions. 13 dealers held a Department 56 sponsored Village Gathering. The vans were sold at these events. The other van was for the Lemon Tree Shop. They were sold to members of the store's Collectors Club. Each of the 14 vans had the store's logo on the left side.

VAN	ITEM #	GREENBOOK TRUMKT PRICE
LEMON TREE	721-8	$ 60.00
BACHMAN'S	729-3	70.00
THE CHRISTMAS DOVE	730-7	60.00
LOCK STOCK & BARREL	731-5	110.00
THE INCREDIBLE CHRISTMAS PLACE	732-3	80.00
THE LIMITED EDITION	733-1	70.00
ROBERT'S CHRISTMAS WONDERLAND	734-0	60.00
FORTUNOFF	735-8	115.00
NORTH POLE CITY	736-6	60.00
BRONNER'S CHRISTMAS WONDERLAND	737-4	60.00
WILLIAM GLEN	738-2	60.00
EUROPEAN IMPORTS	739-0	60.00
THE WINDSOR SHOPPE	740-4	60.00
STATS	741-2	60.00

HVA94-131

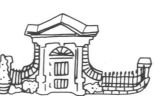

MICKEY & MINNIE

Mickey and Minnie characters welcome guests to the Disney Theme Parks.

HVA94-132

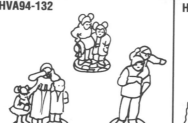

DISNEY PARK FAMILY

A family enjoys the sights and sounds of Disney. Dad has one child hoisted on his shoulders. Mom is taking a photograph.

HVA94-133

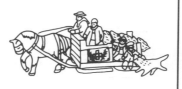

OLDE WORLD ANTIQUES GATE

Wrought iron fence and brick base lead from either side to large wooden door.

HVA94-134

POLKA FEST

Couple dances while two play songs. Boy sings along.

HVA94-135

LAST MINUTE DELIVERY

Two elves pump a hand car in order to rush two cars full of dolls and teddy bears to Santa. A third elf hangs on at the back of the last car.

HVA94-136

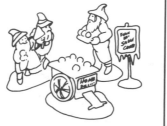

SNOW CONE ELVES

An elf makes a delivery of snow cones to other elves. Cart holds more cones. Icicles cling to the bottom of the sign.

HVA94-137

OVER THE RIVER AND THROUGH THE WOODS

Children and their father take their Christmas tree home by a horse-drawn wooden sleigh. Their dog runs along side.

HVA94-138

THE OLD MAN AND THE SEA

Two children listen closely as the man tells stories of the sea Boy holds telescope.

ART CHART #	NAME	ITEM #	MATERIAL	SET?	!	MARKET STATUS	ORIGINAL SRP	GREENBOOK TRUMKT PRICE
	VARIATIONS/MISC/COLLECTOR NOTES							
HVA94-131	MICKEY & MINNIE (1994) (DPV)	5353-8	Porcelain	SET OF 2		CURRENT	$ 22.50	$ 22.50
HVA94-132	DISNEY PARK FAMILY (1994) (DPV)	5354-6	Porcelain	SET OF 3		CURRENT	32.50	32.50
HVA94-133	OLDE WORLD ANTIQUES GATE (1994) (DPV)	5355-4	Porcelain	NO		CURRENT	15.00	15.00
HVA94-134	POLKA FEST (1994) (ALP)	5607-3	Porcelain	SET OF 3		CURRENT	30.00	30.00
HVA94-135	LAST MINUTE DELIVERY (1994) (NP)	5636-7	Porcelain	SET OF 3		SEE BELOW*	35.00	---
	*Never shipped due to production problems.							
HVA94-136	SNOW CONE ELVES (1994) (NP)	5637-5	Porcelain	SET OF 4		CURRENT	30.00	30.00
HVA94-137	OVER THE RIVER AND THROUGH THE WOODS (1994) (NE)	5654-5	Porcelain	NO		CURRENT	35.00	35.00
HVA94-138	THE OLD MAN AND THE SEA (1994) (NE)	5655-3	Porcelain	SET OF 3		CURRENT	25.00	25.00

HVA94-139

TWO RIVERS BRIDGE

Wooden bridge on 3 sets of pilings over 2 rivers. Horses, carriages and carts use center. Walkers use side passages.

HVA94-140

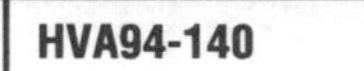

WINTER SLEIGHRIDE

Two boys skate along as they pull their friend in a one person sleigh.

HVA94-141

CHELSEA MARKET MISTLETOE MONGER AND CART

Vendor sells greens from basket as wife sells from cart.

HVA94-142

CHELSEA MARKET CURIOSITIES MONGER AND CART

Vendor sells everything from toys to clocks to quilts.

HVA94-143

PORTOBELLO ROAD PEDDLERS

Peddlers carry wares in baskets or on poles to sell to passing villagers.

HVA94-144

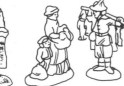

THATCHERS

One worker carries thatch up ladder to roof as helper lifts next bundle.

HVA94-145

A PEACEFUL GLOW ON CHRISTMAS EVE

Clergyman and assistant sell candles for church service.

HVA94-146

CHRISTMAS CAROL HOLIDAY TRIMMING SET

Villagers carry home holiday greens and help decorate area gates, fences, trees and posts.

ART CHART #	NAME	ITEM #	MATERIAL	SET?	💡	MARKET STATUS	ORIGINAL SRP	GREENBOOK TRUMKT PRICE
	VARIATIONS/MISC/COLLECTOR NOTES							
HVA94-139	TWO RIVERS BRIDGE (1994) (NE)	5656-1	Prcln/Resin	NO		CURRENT	$ 35.00	$ 35.00
HVA94-140	WINTER SLEIGHRIDE (1994) (DV)	5825-4	Porcelain	NO		CURRENT	18.00	18.00
HVA94-141	CHELSEA MARKET MISTLETOE MONGER & CART (1994) (DV)	5826-2	Porcelain	SET OF 2		CURRENT	25.00	25.00
HVA94-142	CHELSEA MARKET CURIOSITIES MONGER & CART (1994) (DV)	5827-0	Porcelain	SET OF 2		CURRENT	27.50	27.50
HVA94-143	PORTOBELLO ROAD PEDDLERS (1994) (DV)	5828-9	Porcelain	SET OF 3		CURRENT	27.50	27.50
HVA94-144	THATCHERS (1994) (DV)	5829-7	Porcelain	SET OF 3		CURRENT	35.00	35.00
HVA94-145	A PEACEFUL GLOW ON CHRISTMAS EVE (1994) (DV)	5830-0	Porcelain	SET OF 3		CURRENT	30.00	30.00
HVA94-146	CHRISTMAS CAROL HOLIDAY TRIMMING SET (1994) (DV)	5831-9	Porcelain	SET OF 21		CURRENT	65.00	65.00

HVA94-147

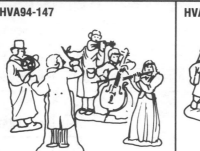

CHAMBER ORCHESTRA
Musicians fill square or park with joyous holiday songs.

HVA94-148

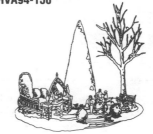

HOLIDAY FIELD TRIP
Five children walk along with their teacher as they visit the many sights of the City.

HVA94-149

HOT DOG VENDOR
A street vendor sells hot dogs to a mother and child as they walk along the city's streets.

HVA94-150

ALL AROUND THE PARK
People walk on pathway around central tree. Stone wall with archway surrounds park.

HVA95-151

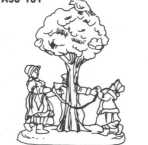

PARTRIDGE IN A PEAR TREE
Three children dance around tree as a partridge sits on top.

HVA95-152

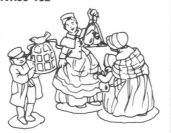

TWO TURTLE DOVES
Woman carries two turtle doves and boy carries cage. Another woman and daughter watch.

HVA94-153

Out of order! Late addition

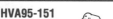

VILLAGE PORCELAIN PINE TREES

ART CHART #	NAME	ITEM #	MATERIAL	SET?	💡	MARKET STATUS	ORIGINAL SRP	GREENBOOK TRUMKT PRICE
	VARIATIONS/MISC/COLLECTOR NOTES							
HVA94-147	CHAMBER ORCHESTRA (1994) (CIC)	5884-0	Porcelain	SET OF 4		CURRENT	$ 37.50	$ 37.50
HVA94-148	HOLIDAY FIELD TRIP (1992) (CIC)	5885-8	Porcelain	SET OF 3		CURRENT	27.50	27.50
HVA94-149	HOT DOG VENDOR (1994) (CIC)	5886-6	Porcelain	SET OF 3		CURRENT	27.50	27.50
HVA94-150	ALL AROUND THE PARK (1994) (HV)	5247-7	Porcelain	SET OF 18		CURRENT	95.00	95.00
	UL approved switched cord. Hidden motor allows 7 figures to move in 2 directions along a cobblestone walk.							
HVA95-151	PARTRIDGE IN A PEAR TREE (1995) (DV)	5835-1	Porcelain	NO		CURRENT	35.00	35.00
	#I, THE 12 DAYS OF DICKENS' VILLAGE.							
HVA95-152	TWO TURTLE DOVES (1995) (DV)	5836-0	Porcelain	SET OF 4		CURRENT	32.50	32.50
	#II, THE 12 DAYS OF DICKENS' VILLAGE.							
HVA95-153	VILLAGE PORCELAIN PINE TREES (1994)	5215-5	Porcelain	SET OF 2		CURRENT	15.00	15.00
Out of order! Late addition								

Page 211

[1] There are 3 versions of the **Carolers**:

- *1st issue* - white post, viola is very light with dark brown trim, very little detail in figures, made in Taiwan.
- *2nd issue* - black post, viola is one color, slightly more detail in figures, made in Taiwan.
- *3rd issue* - black post, viola has darker trim, largest of 3 sets, made in Philippines.

Page 211

[2] There are 2 versions of the **Sleighride**:

- *1st issue* - original sleeve reads, "Dickens Sleighride" - man has a narrow white scarf with red polka dots.
- *2nd issue* - man's scarf and lapels are white with red polka dots. Gray horse is more spotted.

Page 217

[3] There are 3 versions of the **Dover Coach**:

- *1st issue* - Coachman has no mustache, wheels are crude, made in Taiwan, GREENBOOK TRUMARKET PRICE @ $110.
- *2nd issue* - Coachman has mustache, wheels are more round, made in Taiwan, two long recesses on underside of base, GNBK TRUMKT PRICE @ $65.
- *3rd issue* - Coachman has mustache, wheels are round, made in Sri Lanka @ $75.

Pages 233 & 235

[4] There were two different sets of **Churchyard Gate & Fences** introduced in 1992:

- The first one, "Churchyard Fence & Gate" (1992 - 1992), Set of 3, was Item # 5563-8. It was a midyear introduction and a GCC Exclusive. The set of 3 included one gate, one wall, and one corner. This version was pictured in the Quarterly in gray but was shipped in brown.
- The second one, "Churchyard Gate And Fence" (1992 - Current), Set of 3, is Item # 5806-8 and includes one gate and two corners.
- There is also "Churchyard Fence Extensions" (1992 - Current), Set of 4, Item #5807-6, which is four straight wall pieces.

NOTES

ADDITIONAL VILLAGE ACCESSORIES . . .

TREES . . .

	Item No.	Description	Size	Price
	5111-0	Christmas Wreaths	Set of 8 1" & .75"	Discontinued
	5112-8	SV Garland Trim	3 pcs/pkg Each pc 24" long	Discontinued
	5115-2	Frosted Topiary Village Garden	Set of 8 4 cones, 4 ovals	Discontinued
	5175-6	Frosted Norway Pines	Set of 3 7", 9", & 11"	$ 12.95/set
	5181-0	Bare Branch Winter Oak, Small	Each 4.25"	Discontinued
	5182-9	Bare Branch Winter Oak, Large	Each 7.75"	Discontinued
	5183-7	Sisal Tree Set	Set of 7 4 cones & 3 ovals	Discontinued
	5184-5	Winter Oak Tree with 2 Red Birds	Each	Discontinued

	Item #	Description	Size	Price
	5185-3	Topiary Garden Sisal	36 pc asst 2.5", 4", 6", 8", & 12"	Discontinued
	5192-6	Village Potted Topiary Pair	2/pkg 4.75"	Discontinued
	5200-0	Frosted Topiary Cone Trees, Large	2/pkg 11.5"	$ 12.50/pkg
	5201-9	Frosted Topiary Cone Trees, Medium	Set of 4 2 @ 7.5" & 2 @ 6"	10.00/set
	5202-7	Frosted Topiary Trees, Large	Set of 8 4" ea - 4 cones, 4 oblong	12.50/set
	5203-5	Frosted Topiary Trees, Small	Set of 8 4 @ 2" round, 4 @ 3" high	7.50/set
	5205-1	Village Evergreen Trees	Set of 3 3.25", 4.25", & 6.5"	12.95/set
	5216-7	Village Winter Birch Tree	Each 11.5"	12.50/ea
	5218-3	Village Porcelain Pine, Large	Each 8.75"	12.50/ea

Item # = New for 1995

. . . ADDITIONAL VILLAGE ACCESSORIES . . .

. . . *TREES continued* . . .

	5219-1	Village Porcelain Pine, Small	Each 7"	$ 10.00/ea
	5221-3	Pine Cone Trees	Set of 2 8.75" & 7.25"	15.00/set
	5231-0	Frosted Spruce Tree	Each 15"	12.50/ea
	5232-9	Frosted Spruce Tree	Each 22"	27.50/ea
	5241-8	Village Frosted Bare Branch Tree, Small	Each 9.5"	6.50/ea
	5242- 6	Village Frosted Bare Branch Tree, Large	Each 13"	12.50/ea
	5243-4	Village Frosted Bare Branch Tree, w/25 Lights	Each 9"	17.50/ea
	5246-9	Village Pencil Pines	Set of 3 12", 8", 5"	15.00/set

	Item #	Description	Size	Price
	5248--5	Spruce Tree Forest	Set of 4 16" x 14"	$ 25.00/set
	5249-3	Village Frosted Zig-Zag Tree, White	Set of 3 9", 7", 4.5"	15.00/set
	5250-7	Village Frosted Zig-Zag Tree, Green	Set of 3 9", 7.5", 4.5"	15.00/set
	5254-0	Village Autumn Maple Tree	Each 11"	15.00/ea
	5255-8	Snowy White Pine Tree, Small	Each 18"	15.00/ea
	5256-6	Snowy White Pine Tree, Large	Each 24"	20.00/ea
	5419-4	Sisal Wreaths	6/pkg 1" diameter	4.00/pkg
	5527-1	Pole Pine Forest	Set of 5 4 trees in a snow base, 10" x 5" x 12"	48.00/set
	5528-0	Pole Pine Tree, Small	Each 8"	10.00/ea

Item # = New for 1995

. . . ADDITIONAL VILLAGE ACCESSORIES . . .

	Item No.	Description	Size	Price
		. . . TREES continued		
	5529-8	Pole Pine Tree, Large	Each 10.5"	$12.50/ea
	6582-0	Papier-Mache Frosted Evergreen Trees	Set of 3	16.00/set
	6595-1	Spruce Tree with Wooden Base, Small	Each 6"	3.50/ea
	6597-8	Spruce Tree with Wooden Base, Medium	Each 9"	5.00/ea
	6598-6	Spruce Tree with Wooden Base, Large	Each 12"	7.00/ea
		ELECTRICAL		
	5213-2	"Lights Out" Remote Control	4" x 2.75" Turns lights on/off in up to 60 houses at once	Discontinued
	5502-6	AC/DC Adapter for Battery Operated Accessories		$14.00/ea

	Item #	Description	Size	Price
	9902-8	Single Cord Set with Light Bulb		$ 3.50/set
	9924-4	Replacement Light Bulbs	3/pkg	2.00/pkg
	9926-0	Battery Operated Light	Each 6 watts, 12 volts	Discontinued
	9927-9	6 Socket Lite Set with Bulbs	Each	12.50/set
	9933-3	Multi-Outlet Plug Strip, 6 Outlets	Each 12" x 2" x 1.5"	10.00/ea
LAMPS/LIGHTS . . .				
	3636-6	Heritage Village Street Lamp Set (2 "AA" Batteries)	6/pkg Cord 60" long, lamps 2.25" tall	$10.00/pkg
	5206-0	Candles by the Doorstep (2 "AA" Batteries)	4/pkg 2.25"	Discontinued
	5215-9	Village Mini Lights	14 bulbs 27" long cord	12.50/set

Item # = New for 1995

. . . ADDITIONAL VILLAGE ACCESSORIES . . .

. . . *LAMPS/LIGHTS continued*

	Item	Description	Qty/Size	Price
	5416-0	Yard Lights (2 Santas, 2 Snowmen)	Set of 4 1.75"	Discontinued
	5500-0	Traffic Light (2 "C" Batteries)	2/pkg 4.25"	$ 11.00/pkg
	5501-8	Railroad Crossing Sign (2 "C" Batteries)	2/pkg 4.25"	12.50/pkg
	5503-4	Old World Streetlamp (2 "C" Batteries)	4/pkg 4"	Discontinued
	5504-2	Turn Of The Century Lamppost (2 "C" Batteries)	4/pkg 4"	16.00/pkg
	5505-0	Turn of the Century Lamppost (2 "C" Batteries)	6/pkg 4"	Discontinued
	5993-5	Streetlamp Wrapped in Garland	2/pkg 4"	Discontinued
	5996-0	Double Street Lamps (2 "C" Batteries)	4/pkg 3.5"	13.00/pkg

SNOW

	Item #	Description	Size	Price
	4995-6	Blanket of New Fallen Snow	2' x 5' x 1"	$ 7.50/ea
	4996-4	"Let It Snow" Crystals, Plastic Snow	8 oz box	Discontinued
	4998-1	Real Plastic Snow	7 oz bag	3.00/bag
	4999-9	Real Plastic Snow	2 lb box	10.00/box

FENCES . . .

	Item #	Description	Size	Price
	5204-3	Snow Fence, Flexible Wood & Wire	Each 2" high x 36" long	$ 7.00/ea
	5207-8	Frosty Tree-Lined Picket Fence	Each 5.75" x 2.5", 3 posts & 3 attached trees	6.50/ea
	5212-4	Tree-Lined Courtyard Fence	Each 1.5" high x 4" long	4.00/ea

Item # = New for 1995

. . . ADDITIONAL VILLAGE ACCESSORIES . . .

. . . *FENCES continued*

Item No.	Description	Quantity / Size	Price
5220-5	Courtyard Fence with Steps	Each 1.25" high x 4.25" long	$ 4.00/ea
5234-5	Chain Link Fence with Gate	Set of 3 2", 4.5"	12.00/set
5235-3	Chain Link Fence Extensions	Set of 4 4.5"	15.00/set
5252-3	Victorian Wrought Iron Fence w/Gate	Set of 5 5.5" x 3"	15.00/set
5253-1	Victorian Wrought Iron Fence Extension	Each 3"	2.50/ea
5506-9	Lamp Post/Fence (2 "AA" Batteries)	Set of 10 2 lamps, 4 posts, 4 fence pcs	Discontinued
5508-5	Lamp Post/Fence Extension	Set of 12 6 posts & 6 fence pcs	Discontinued
5514-0	Village Wrought Iron Gate with Fence, Green	Set of 9 gate & 4 fence pcs w/4 posts, 9.25" x 3"	15.00/set

	Item #	Description	Quantity / Size	Price
	5515-8	Village Wrought Iron Fence Extension	Set of 9 4 fence pieces & 5 posts, 9.25" x 3"	$ 12.50/set
	5541-7	Subway Entrance	Each 4.5" x 2.75" x 4.5"	15.00/ea
	5998-6	Wrought Iron Fence (White & Black or White & Green)	Each 4" long	2.50/ea
	5999-4	Wrought Iron Fence (White & Black)	4/pkg 4" long	10.00/pkg
		MOUNTAINS		
	5226-4	Village Mountains with Frosted Sisal Trees, Small	Set of 5 12" x 10.5" x 8", 4 trees	$ 32.50/set
	5227-2	Village Mountains with Frosted Sisal Trees, Medium	Set of 8 22" x 12" x 10.5", 7 trees, 1 niche to display Village piece	65.00/set
	5228-0	Village Mountains with Frosted Sisal Trees, Large	Set of 14 35" x 13" x 15.5", 13 trees, can accomodate 3 lighted pieces	150.00/set
	5257-4	Village Mountain Backdrop (w/o Trees)	Set of 2 27" x 11", 22" x 9.5"	65.00/set

Item # = New for 1995

. . . ADDITIONAL VILLAGE ACCESSORIES . . .

TRIMS

Item #	Description	Quantity / Size	Price
5109-8	Village Park Bench	Each 2.5"	Discontinued
5110-1	Village Clock (Green or Black)	Each 3.5"	$ 3.00/ea
5208-6	Mylar Skating Pond	2 sheets/pkg 25.25" x 18" each	6.00/pkg
5210-8	Brick Road	2 strips/pkg 4.75" x 36" each	10.00/pkg
5984-6	Cobblestone Road	2 strips/pkg 4.75" x 36" each	10.00/set
5211-6	Acrylic Icicles	4/pkg 18" long each	4.50/pkg
5511-5	"Christmas Eave" Trim (bulb garland, non-electric)	Each 24" long	3.50/ea
5217-5	Tacky Wax	Each 1" diameter x 1" deep tub	2.00/tub

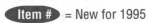

	Item #	Description	Size	Price
	5230-2	Wrought Iron Park Bench	Each 2.25"	$ 5.00/ea
	5233-7	Sled & Skis	Set of 2 2" & 2.25"	6.00/set
	5512-3	Heritage Village Utility Accessories 2 stop signs, 4 parking meters, 2 traffic lights	Set of 8 1.75" - 3"	12.50/set
	5524-7	"Village Sounds" Tape with Speakers	23 minute tape, 12' cord	Discontinued
	5525-5	"Village Sounds" Tape	23 minutes, continuous play	Discontinued
	5417-8	It's A Grand Old Flag	2/pkg 2.25"	4.00/pkg
	5526-3	Heritage Banners	Set of 4, 2 each of 2 1.25"	6.00/set
	948-2	Heritage Village Collection Promotional Logo Banner	Each Giveaway at 1992 events	Promo

= New for 1995

. . . ADDITIONAL VILLAGE ACCESSORIES

VILLAGE BRITE LITES

	5222-1	"I Love My Village"	6.5"	$ 15.00/ea
	5223-0	"Merry Christmas"	7.5"	15.00/ea
	5224-8	Flashing Reindeer, Animated	3.25"	13.50/ea
	5225-6	Village Brite Lites Adapter		10.00/ea
	5236-1	Fence, Animated	Set of 4 11"	25.00/set
	5237-0	Snowman, Animated	3.75"	20.00/ea
	5238-8	Tree, Animated	3.5"	13.50/ea
	5239-6	Santa, Animated	3.5"	20.00/ea

	Item #	Description	Size	Price
	5244-2	Waving Flag, Animated	5"	$ 12.50/ea
	5245-0	20 Red Lights		9.00/ea
DRINK Coca-Cola	5482-8	Coca-Cola Brand Neon Sign	4.5" x 2"	22.50/ea
Department 56	9846-9	Department 56, Animated	5"	10.00 ea

Item # = New for 1995

QUIKREFERENCE - RETIRED PIECES

THE ORIGINAL SNOW VILLAGE RETIRED BUILDINGS

5000-8	1984	Town Hall
5001-3	1979	Mountain Lodge
5001-6	1985	Grocery
5002-1	1979	Gabled Cottage
5002-4	1984	Victorian Cottage
5003-2	1985	Governor's Mansion
5003-9	1979	The Inn
5004-0	1986	Turn Of The Century
5004-7	1979	Country Church
5005-4	1979	Steepled Church
5005-9	1986	Main Street House
5006-2	1979	Small Chalet
5006-7	1989	St. Anthony Hotel & Post Office
5007-0	1979	Victorian House
5007-5	1986	Stratford House
5008-3	1987	Haversham House
5008-8	1979	Mansion
5009-1	1985	Galena House
5009-6	1979	Stone Church
5010-5	1987	River Road House
5011-2	1984	Homestead
5012-0	1980	General Store
5012-1	1986	Delta House
5013-0	1989	Snow Village Factory
5013-8	1980	Cape Cod
5014-6	1986	Nantucket
5015-3	1979	Skating Rink/ Duck Pond Set
5015-6	1986	Bayport
5016-1	1989	Small Double Trees
5017-2	1984	Skating Pond
5019-9	1990	Cathedral Church
5019-9	1984	Street Car
5020-2	1984	Centennial House
5021-0	1984	Carriage House
5022-9	1984	Pioneer Church
5023-7	1984	Swiss Chalet
5024-5	1983	Bank
5025-3	1984	Gingerbread House
5026-1	1984	Village Church
5027-0	1990	Springfield House
5028-8	1986	Gothic Church
5029-6	1985	Parsonage
5030-0	1988	Lighthouse
5031-8	1985	Wooden Church
5032-6	1984	Fire Station
5033-4	1985	English Tudor
5034-2	1985	Congregational Church
5035-0	1986	Trinity Church
5036-9	1985	Summit House
5037-7	1986	New School House
5039-3	1986	Parish Church
5041-5	1986	Waverly Place
5042-3	1986	Twin Peaks
5043-1	1986	2101 Maple
5044-0	1991	Village Market
5045-8	1986	Stucco Bungalow
5046-6	1988	Williamsburg House
5047-4	1987	Plantation House
5048-2	1988	Church Of The Open Door
5049-0	1987	Spruce Place
5050-4	1987	Duplex
5051-2	1988	Depot And Train With 2 Train Cars
5052-0	1987	Ridgewood
5054-2	1982	Victorian
5054-7	1990	Kenwood House
5055-9	1981	Knob Hill
5056-7	1981	Brownstone
5057-5	1981	Log Cabin
5058-3	1984	Countryside Church
5059-1	1980	Stone Church
5060-1	1988	Lincoln Park Duplex
5060-9	1982	School House
5061-7	1981	Tudor House
5062-5	1980	Mission Church
5062-8	1988	Sonoma House
5063-3	1980	Mobile Home
5063-6	1988	Highland Park House
5065-2	1988	Beacon Hill House
5065-8	1982	Giant Trees
5066-0	1988	Pacific Heights House
5066-6	1980	Adobe House
5067-4	1981	Cathedral Church
5067-9	1989	Ramsey Hill House
5068-2	1982	Stone Mill House
5068-7	1988	Saint James Church
5070-9	1982	Colonial Farm House
5071-7	1988	Carriage House
5071-7	1982	Town Church
5072-5	1984	Wooden Clapboard
5073-3	1982	English Cottage
5073-3	1990	Toy Shop
5074-1	1984	Barn

THE ORIGINAL SNOW VILLAGE RETIRED BUILDINGS continued

5076-8	1990	Apothecary
5076-8	1983	Corner Store
5077-6	1983	Bakery
5077-6	1991	Bakery
5078-4	1987	Diner
5078-4	1982	English Church
5080-6	1989	Large Single Tree
5081-4	1983	Gabled House
5081-4	1992	Red Barn
5082-2	1983	Flower Shop
5082-2	1991	Jefferson School
5083-0	1984	New Stone Church
5084-9	1984	Chateau
5085-6	1985	Train Station With 3 Train Cars
5089-0	1992	Farm House
5091-1	1989	Fire Station No. 2
5092-0	1989	Snow Village Resort Lodge
5114-4	1991	Jingle Belle Houseboat
5119-5	1992	Colonial Church
5120-9	1992	North Creek Cottage
5121-7	1990	Maple Ridge Inn
5122-5	1992	Village Station And Train
5123-3	1992	Cobblestone Antique Shop
5124-1	1991	Corner Cafe
5125-0	1990	Single Car Garage
5126-8	1991	Home Sweet Home/ House & Windmill
5127-6	1992	Redeemer Church
5128-4	1991	Service Station
5140-3	1994	Stonehurst House
5141-1	1990	Palos Verdes
5142-0	1993	Paramount Theater
5143-8	1992	Doctor's House
5144-6	1993	Courthouse
5145-4	1992	Village Warming House
5149-7	1992	J. Young's Granary
5151-9	1992	56 Flavors Ice Cream Parlor
5152-7	1992	Morningside House
5153-5	1993	Mainstreet Hardware
5154-3	1993	Village Realty
5155-1	1992	Spanish Mission Church
5156-0	1993	Prairie House
5400-3	1994	Oak Grove Tudor
5401-1	1993	The Honeymooner Motel
5403-8	1994	Southern Colonial
5405-4	1993	Finklea's Finery Costume Shop
5406-2	1994	Jack's Corner Barber Shop
5407-0	1994	Double Bungalow
5421-6	1994	St. Luke's Church
5425-9	1994	Print Shop & Village News

QUIKREFERENCE - RETIRED PIECES

THE ORIGINAL SNOW VILLAGE RETIRED ACCESSORIES

5018-0	1990	Snowman With Broom
5038-5	1985	Scottie With Tree
5040-7	1988	Monks-A-Caroling
5053-9	1987	Singing Nuns
5056-3	1987	Snow Kids Sled, Skis
5057-1	1988	Family Mom/Kids, Goose/Girl
5059-8	1988	Santa/Mailbox
5064-1	1986	Carolers
5069-0	1986	Ceramic Car
5079-2	1986	Ceramic Sleigh
5094-6	1990	Kids Around The Tree
5095-4	1987	Girl/Snowman, Boy
5096-2	1988	Shopping Girls With Packages
5102-0	1988	3 Nuns W/Songbooks
5103-9	1988	Praying Monks
5104-7	1989	Children In Band
5105-5	1990	Caroling Family
5107-1	1990	Christmas Children
5108-0	1989	For Sale Sign
5109-8	1993	Village Park Bench
5113-6	1990	Snow Kids
5116-0	1992	Man On Ladder Hanging Garland
5117-9	1990	Hayride
5118-7	1990	School Children
5129-2	1990	Apple Girl/ Newspaper Boy
5130-6	1991	Woodsman And Boy
5131-4	1992	Doghouse/Cat In Garbage Can
5133-0	1991	Water Tower
5134-9	1993	Kids Decorating The Village Sign
5136-5	1990	Woody Station Wagon
5137-3	1991	School Bus, Snow Plow
5147-0	1992	Choir Kids
5148-9	1990	Special Delivery
5158-6	1993	Down The Chimney He Goes
5159-4	1993	Sno-Jet Snowmobile
5160-8	1992	Sleighride
5161-6	1992	Here We Come A Caroling
5162-4	1992	Home Delivery
5163-2	1993	Fresh Frozen Fish
5168-3	1991	Kids Tree House
5169-1	1992	Bringing Home The Tree
5170-5	1991	Skate Faster Mom
5172-1	1991	Through The Woods
5173-0	1991	Statue Of Mark Twain
5174-8	1991	Calling All Cars
5179-9	1990	Mailbox
5180-2	1994	Village Winter Birds
5197-7	1992	Special Delivery
5408-9	1994	Wreaths for Sale
5409-7	1993	Winter Fountain
5410-0	1994	Cold Weather Sports
5411-9	1992	Come Join The Parade
5412-7	1992	Village Marching Band
5413-5	1994	Christmas Cadillac
5414-3	1993	Snowball Fort
5415-1	1993	Country Harvest
5418-6	1994	Village Greetings
5430-5	1994	Nanny And The Preschoolers
5435-6	1994	We're Going to a Christmas Pageant
6459-9	1984	Monks-A-Caroling
8183-3	1991	Sisal Tree Lot

MEADOWLAND RETIRED PIECES

5050-0	1980	Thatched Cottage
5051-8	1980	Countryside Church
5052-6	1980	Aspen Trees
5053-4	1980	Sheep

DICKENS' VILLAGE RETIRED BUILDINGS

5550-6	1992	David Copperfield
5550-6	1992	Mr. Wickfield Solicitor
5550-6	1992	Betsy Trotwood's Cottage
5550-6	1992	Peggotty's Seaside Cottage
5553-0	1993	Oliver Twist
5553-0	1993	Brownlow House
5553-0	1993	Maylie Cottage
5557-3	1994	Nephew Fred's Flat
5567-0	1992	Bishops Oast House
5583-2	1991	Cobles Police Station
5584-0	1992	Theatre Royal
5900-5	1989	Barley Bree
5900-5	1989	Farmhouse
5900-5	1989	Barn
5902-1	1990	Counting House & Silas Thimbleton Barrister
5916-1	1988	Kenilworth Castle
5924-2	1990	Cobblestone Shops
5924-2	1990	The Wool Shop
5924-2	1990	Booter And Cobbler
5924-2	1990	T. Wells Fruit & Spice Shop
5925-0	1991	Nicholas Nickleby
5925-0	1991	Nicholas Nickleby Cottage
5925-0	1991	Wackford Squeers Boarding School
5926-9	1993	Merchant Shops
5926-9	1993	Poulterer
5926-9	1993	Geo. Weeton Watchmaker
5926-9	1993	The Mermaid Fish Shoppe
5926-9	1993	White Horse Bakery
5926-9	1993	Walpole Tailors
5927-7	1991	Ivy Glen Church
6507-2	1989	Dickens' Lane Shops
6507-2	1989	Thomas Kersey Coffee House
6507-2	1989	Cottage Toy Shop
6507-2	1989	Tuttle's Pub
6508-0	1990	Blythe Pond Mill House
6515-3	1988	The Original Shops Of Dickens' Village
6515-3	1988	Crowntree Inn
6515-3	1988	Candle Shop
6515-3	1988	Green Grocer
6515-3	1988	Golden Swan Baker
6515-3	1988	Bean And Son Smithy Shop
6515-3	1988	Abel Beesley Butcher
6515-3	1988	Jones & Co. Brush & Basket Shop
6516-1	1989	Dickens' Village Church
6518-8	1988	Dickens' Cottages
6518-8	1988	Thatched Cottage
6518-8	1988	Stone Cottage
6518-8	1988	Tudor Cottage
6528-5	1989	Chadbury Station And Train
6549-8	1989	Brick Abbey

ALPINE VILLAGE RETIRED BUILDINGS

5615-4	1993	Bahnhof
5952-8	1989	Josef Engel Farmhouse
6541-2	1991	Alpine Church

BACHMAN'S RETIRED BUILDINGS

670-0	1988	Home Town Boarding House
671-8	1988	Home Town Church
672-6	1989	Home Town Drugstore

QUIKREFERENCE - RETIRED PIECES

NEW ENGLAND VILLAGE RETIRED BUILDINGS

5930-7	1994	Craggy Cove Lighthouse
5931-5	1989	Weston Train Station
5939-0	1990	Cherry Lane Shops
5939-0	1990	Ben's Barbershop
5939-0	1990	Otis Hayes Butcher Shop
5939-0	1990	Anne Shaw Toys
5940-4	1991	Ada's Bed And Boarding House
5942-0	1991	Berkshire House
5943-9	1992	Jannes Mullet Amish Farm House
5944-7	1992	Jannes Mullet Amish Barn
5946-3	1994	Shingle Creek House
5954-4	1993	Sleepy Hollow
5954-4	1993	Sleepy Hollow School
5954-4	1993	Van Tassel Manor
5954-4	1993	Ichabod Crane's Cottage
5955-2	1993	Sleepy Hollow Church
6530-7	1989	New England Village
6530-7	1989	Apothecary Shop
6530-7	1989	General Store
6530-7	1989	Livery Stable & Boot Shop
6530-7	1989	Steeple Church
6530-7	1989	Brick Town Hall
6530-7	1989	Red Schoolhouse
6530-7	1989	Nathaniel Bingham Fabrics
6538-2	1989	Jacob Adams Farmhouse & Barn
6539-0	1990	Steeple Church
6544-7	1990	Timber Knoll Log Cabin

CHRISTMAS IN THE CITY RETIRED BUILDINGS

5537-9	1994	Wong's in Chinatown
5543-3	1993	Arts Academy
5544-1	1994	The Doctor's Office
5961-7	1989	Sutton Place Brownstones
5962-5	1990	The Cathedral
5963-3	1989	Palace Theatre
5968-4	1991	Chocolate Shoppe
5969-2	1991	City Hall
5970-6	1992	Hank's Market
5972-2	1990	Variety Store
5973-0	1994	Ritz Hotel
5977-3	1992	5607 Park Ave Townhouse
5978-1	1992	5609 Park Ave Townhouse
6512-9	1990	Christmas In The City
6512-9	1990	Toy Shop & Pet Store
6512-9	1990	Bakery
6512-9	1990	Tower Restaurant

NORTH POLE RETIRED BUILDING

5600-6	1993	Santa's Workshop

HERITAGE VILLAGE RETIRED ACCESSORIES

5535-2	1992	Busy Sidewalks
5539-5	1994	'Tis the Season
5545-0	1993	All Around The Town
5551-4	1992	David Copperfield Characters
5554-9	1993	Oliver Twist Characters
5560-3	1994	Come Into The Inn
5570-0	1993	Carolers On The Doorstep
5572-7	1994	Village Sign With Snowman
5578-6	1992	Royal Coach
5579-4	1991	Constables
5580-8	1992	Violet Vendor/ Carolers/ Chestnut Vendor
5604-9	1994	Letters For Santa
5608-1	1993	Trimming The North Pole
5610-3	1993	Santa's Little Helpers
5641-3	1993	Market Day
5804-1	1994	Village Street Peddlers
5901-3	1989	Farm People & Animals
5903-0	1991	Childe Pond And Skaters
5928-5	1990	Fezziwig And Friends
5929-3	1991	Nicholas Nickleby Characters
5934-0	1990	Blacksmith
5938-2	1994	Snow Children
5941-2	1991	Village Harvest People
5945-5	1991	Farm Animals
5948-0	1992	Amish Family
5949-8	1992	Amish Buggy
5950-1	1989	Silo & Hay Shed
5951-0	1989	Ox Sled
5956-0	1992	Sleepy Hollow Characters
5957-9	1991	Organ Grinder
5958-7	1992	Popcorn Vendor
5959-5	1991	River Street Ice House Cart
5960-9	1993	Christmas In The City Sign
5965-0	1990	City People
5966-8	1988	Shopkeepers
5967-6	1988	City Workers
5971-4	1991	City Newsstand
5981-1	1990	Village Train Trestle
5982-0	1993	One Horse Open Sleigh
5983-8	1991	City Bus & Milk Truck
5985-4	1991	Salvation Army Band
5986-2	1990	Woodcutter And Son
5987-0	1994	Red Covered Bridge
6501-3	1990	Christmas Carol Figures
6510-2	1989	Lighted Tree W/ Children & Ladder
6511-0	1990	Sleighride
6526-9	1990	Carolers
6527-7	1986	Village Train
6531-5	1990	Covered Wooden Bridge
6532-3	1990	New England Winter Set
6537-4	1992	Porcelain Trees
6542-0	1992	Alpine Villagers
6545-5	1990	Skating Pond
6546-3	1990	Stone Bridge
6547-1	1989	Village Well & Holy Cross
6569-2	1993	Dickens' Village Sign
6570-6	1993	New England Village Sign
6571-4	1993	Alpine Village Sign
6589-7	1989	Maple Sugaring Shed
6590-0	1990	Dover Coach

QUIKREFERENCE - Ltd Eds, Event Pcs, Annuals & Series

LIMITED EDITIONS

DICKENS' VILLAGE LIMITED EDITIONS:

5585-9 ... Ruth Marion Scotch Woolens . 17,500
5586-7 ... Green Gate Cottage 22,500
5904-8 ... C. Fletcher Public House 12,500
6502-1 ... Norman Church 3,500
6519-6 ... Dickens' Village Mill 2,500
6568-4 ... Chesterton Manor House 7,500

NEW ENGLAND VILLAGE LIMITED EDITIONS:

6543-1 ... Smythe Woolen Mill 7,500

CHRISTMAS IN THE CITY LIMITED EDITIONS:

5549-2 ... Cathedral Church Of St. Mark 17,500 Announced, Actual Production 3,024
5974-9 ... Dorothy's Dress Shop 12,500

EVENT PIECES (all are also Annuals)

5530-1	Gate House	1992
9871-0	Postern	1994

ANNUALS

5441-0	Nantucket Renovation	1993
5809-2	Boarding & Lodging School	1993
9872-8	Dedlock Arms Ornament	1994
5477-1	Santa Comes To Town	1995
9870-1	Falstaff Inn Ornament	1995

SERIES

AMERICAN ARCHITECTURE SERIES (SV)

5156-0 Prairie House
5157-8 Queen Anne Victorian
5403-8 Southern Colonial
5404-6 Gothic Farmhouse
5437-2 Craftsman Cottage
5465-8 Federal House

CHARLES DICKENS' SIGNATURE SERIES (HV) (all are also Annuals)

5750-9	Crown & Cricket Inn	1992
5751-7	The Pied Bull Inn	1993
5752-5	Dedlock Arms	1994
5753-3	Sir John Falstaff Inn	1995

GLOSSARY

Glossary

A Christmas Carol

A Christmas story written in 1843 by Charles Dickens; a grouping within Dickens' Village, introduced in 1986

Accessory

Any of the characters, animals, non-lit structures, etc. that are sold to compliment and complete any one of the villages

Adobe

Sun-dried, unburned brick made of clay and straw; a building made with this type of brick; Adobe - Snow Village

Allocation

A specific number of goods, either in quantity or dollar amount, that a dealer is allowed to purchase

Allotment

Same as allocation

Alpine Village

Third of the Heritage Villages, introduced in 1986; depicts villages found in the Alps

American Architecture Series

A series within The Original Snow Village introduced in 1990

Amish

A Mennonite sect founded in the 17th century; a grouping of buildings and accessories in the New England Village

Annual

A collectible issued for a single year - sometimes to commemorate an anniversary, holiday or other special date

Artist Proof

Usually, the first piece in the production of an edition that has been reviewed and approved by the artist; most often with lithographs or prints

Attachments

Any part of a building or accessory that has been molded separately and then added to the main body with liquid clay

Bachman's

A Minneapolis-based floral supply company from which Department 56 was begun; was the parent company of Department 56 until 1992

Bachman's Hometown Series

Introduced in 1987, a short-lived series of three buildings produced exclusively for sale by Bachman's retail stores

Bachman's Village Gathering

An event held each summer in Minneapolis featuring Department 56 Villages and related items

Backstamp

The information located on the back of a plate or other item that includes the manufacturer's name, name of the item, year of issue, etc.

Bas-Relief
A flat collectible with a raised design

Bisque
A porcelain, generally white, that has no glaze or enamel applied to it

Bottom Stamp
Specific information embossed on the bottom of a piece containing D56 logo, year of introduction, etc.; became standard in 1988; previously could have been hand-carved or even non-existent

Box
The foam container in which the village pieces are shipped and stored

CCP
Common reference for Cold Cast Porcelain

Case Mold
Often referred to as the master mold, it is produced with a high density composite material that will not wear out as quickly as the more porous production molds

Casting
The initial step in the production of a porcelain collectible, liquid clay is poured into a production mold and, after being allowed to dry, removed as a semi-firm piece

Ceramic
A form of clay finished by firing at a high temperature

Certificate of Authenticity
A document that attests to a piece being genuine and its place within a limited edition or production

Charles Dickens Heritage Collection
A portion of the royalties received by the Dickens Heritage Foundation from the sale of these items are donated for the benefit of the sick and needy in both England and the U.S.

Charles Dickens Heritage Foundation
Created in 1991 by the great-great grandson of Charles Dickens, Christopher Dickens, and his wife, Jeanne-Marie, to continue the charitable work of Dickens

Charles Dickens Signature Series
Any of the various products displaying the Crest and Badge and "CD" emblem

China
A high quality clay fired at a high temperature; also known as porcelain; the third country to produce Department 56 buildings

Chip
The location on a piece where a small portion of porcelain has been broken off usually leaving a rough area

Christmas in the City
Fourth of the Heritage Villages, introduced in 1989; depicts a large city, possibly Manhattan

Glossary continued

Clay

Any of the earthen materials used to make ceramic items, it becomes hard when fired at high temperatures

Cold Cast Porcelain (aka ccp)

A porcelain piece that is produced by mixing a resin with porcelain dust and forcing it into a mold under high pressure where it is allowed to harden without firing in a kiln; any of the 25 Dickens' Village and 13 New England Village CCP pieces

Collectors Club

A formal or informal group consisting of people who collect the same collectible

Commemorative

An item specially made to mark an event, anniversary or holiday

Cutter

A small, light sleigh

David Copperfield

A story written by Charles Dickens; a grouping in Dickens' Village introduced in 1989 and retired in 1992

Disney Park Village Series

Introduced in 1994, it is the seventh Heritage Village

Charles Dickens

English author born in 1812, died in 1870, he penned many well known stories including *A Christmas Carol* plus others referred to within the Dickens' Village; for whom Department 56's first porcelain village is named

Jeanne-Marie Dickens

Wife of Christopher Dickens, the great-great grandson of Charles Dickens; Founder and President of the Charles Dickens Heritage Foundation

Dickens' Village

First of the Heritage Villages, introduced in 1984, depicts the England written about by Dickens

Discontinued

Refers to an item that is no longer in production

Earthenware

A form of porcelain usually glazed and fired

Error

Something that has been incorrectly done when producing a piece; this sometimes, but not always, adds to the value or collectibility of a piece; same as mistake

Exclusives

Actually early releases, these pieces are made available to a select group of dealers in the fall and then to the remaining dealers the following January.

Factory Flaw

Any defect, usually a chip or crack, that happened when the piece was being produced

Fire

To heat at high temperatures and harden a ceramic or clay material in a kiln

Firing Crack

A crack in a ceramic or porcelain product that occurred during the firing of the piece

Firing Period

The length of time in which a manufacturer produces a fired product

First Issue

The first item in a series

GCC

Gift Creation Concepts, a syndicated catalog group with retail store members throughout the country

Glaze

A liquid material that is applied after firing and before decorating to create a shine

Heritage Village

Encompasses Dickens' Village, New England Village, Alpine Village, Christmas In The City, Little Town Of Bethlehem Collection, North Pole Collection, Disney Park Village Series and their accessories; introduced in 1984

History List

The common reference for the Snow Village and Heritage Village brochures that list the entire collections along with their issue date, SRP and retirement date

Incised

A design that is cut into a piece to create a backstamp or decoration

International Collectible Exposition

The nation's largest collectible show that is held each summer in the Midwest and alternates each spring between Long Beach, CA and Secaucus, NJ

Issue Price

The suggested retail price of an item when it is first introduced

Key Dealer

The deignation for a specific level of Dept. 56 dealer - either "Gold" or "Village" Key

Knock-off

A copy of an original, usually crude in quality

Limited Edition

An edition that is restricted in quantity by a limit of a specific number

List Price

Usually the suggested retail price determined by the manufacturer

Lite-Ups

Small porcelain replicas of 17 Dickens' Village and 13 New England Village buildings; each has a hole and clip on the bottom so that it may be clipped to a tree branch and a mini tree light inserted

Glossary continued

Little Town of Bethlehem

Introduced in 1987, it is the fifth of the Heritage Villages

Master Mold

Often referred to as the case mold, it is produced with a high density composite material that will not wear out as quickly as the more porous production molds

Meadowland Series

A ceramic "springtime" series introduced in 1979 and retired in 1980; consisting of two buildings and two sets of accessories, it resembles Snow Village pieces without snow

Midyear Introductions

Announcements in May of the new pieces that will be available in the Fall

Mint Condition

Signifies that a piece is in its original, like-new condition with all documentation, box and sleeve

Mistake

Something that has been incorrectly done when producing a piece; this sometimes, but not always, adds to the value or collectibility of a piece; same as error

Mold

The form in which an item is created

Mother Mold

This mold is taken from the clay model and is made with superfine plaster to allow fine details to be impressed into the mold

Ms. Lit-Town

Department 56's pseudonym for their Public Relations person, Judith Price

NALED

Acronym for an organization for collectible retailers, the National Association Of Limited Edition Dealers

New England Village

Second of the Heritage Villages, introduced in 1986, depicts New England, though it also represents the Hudson Valley and Pennsylvania

Nicholas Nickleby

A story written by Charles Dickens; a grouping in Dickens' Village introduced in 1988 and retired in 1991

North Pole Collection

A Department 56 Village introduced in 1990 depicting the fanciful world of Santa Claus and the North Pole

Oast House

A building in which hops are dried to produce beer and ale

Oliver Twist

A story written by Charles Dickens; a grouping in Dickens' Village introduced in 1991

One Village Place

The common reference address for Department 56's headquarters in Eden Prairie, Minnasota - actuall adress is 6436 City West Parkway

Original Snow Village

The first village marketed by Department 56, made of ceramic with a glazed finish, introduced in 1976, depicts "Anytown, USA"

Overglaze

A decoration, usually painted by hand, that is applied after the original glazing and firing of a piece

Paste

Porcelain in its raw form before shaping and firing

Pied

An English term meaning spotted as in The Pied Bull Inn

Production Mold

A mold of porous plaster used to create the actual piece, the mold absorbs the moisture from the liquid clay during the firing process, these molds are replaced after 30 - 40 castings

Proof

A piece produced to check the quality of the production; in a run of limited editions, proofs are marked as such and not numbered

Prototype

An original hand-sculpted model

Quarterly

The Department 56 magazine that is produced four times a year

Restoration

The repair process performed to mend a damaged collectible

Retired

Refers to a piece that is no longer being produced and will not be in the future

Room Hopping

Roaming from room to room in a hotel during an event to buy secondary pieces

Second

Any item that is not of acceptable quality

Secondary Market

The market in which retired and limited pieces are purchased, sold or traded either through a company or individuals

Secondary Market Broker

A company or person who advertises and sells collectibles for collectors and receives a commission for doing so

Secondary Market Dealer

A company or person who sells secondary pieces that they own

Glossary continued

Secondary Market Price

The price that a retired collectible is commanding on the secondary market

Shrinkage

The amount of reduction in a piece when it is fired

Sisal

A hemplike fiber obtained from the agave plant

Sleeve

The cardboard cover, printed with product identification, that slips over the styrofoam packing box

Slip

Liquid clay that is poured into a mold or used to adhere two pieces together

Special Event Piece

A piece that is produced to be sold only at a specific event or series of events

Sri Lanka

The location where the third Dover Coach was produced

Swap 'n Sell

An event organized so that collectors may sell or swap items with each other

Tacky Wax

A pliable wax used to secure accessories in place yet allows easy removal

Taiwan

The first country to produce Department 56 villages

Topiary

Trees and bushes that are cut and trimmed into shapes

Translucency

The quality or degree in which light shines through a non-transparent object

Variation

A change in form, mold or color of a piece from the first issue to subsequent issues

Village Gathering

A large show where Dept. 56 collectors attend seminars, secondary market Swap & Sells and a variety of other Dept. 56 related events